D1462612

CZECHOSLOVAK ACADEMY OF SCIENCES

Quido Záruba, Vojtěch Mencl

Landslides
and their
control

CZECHOSLOVAK ACADEMY OF SCIENCES

SCIENTIFIC EDITOR
Dr. Ladislav Čepek

Quido Záruba,
Vojtěch Mencl

LANDSLIDES
and
THEIR CONTROL

ELSEVIER
Amsterdam • London • New York
in coedition with

ACADEMIA
Publishing House of the
Czechoslovak Academy of Sciences
PRAGUE
1969

Distribution of this book is being handled by the following publishers

for the U.S.A. and Canada
American Elsevier Publishing Company, Inc.
New York

for the East European Countries, China, Northern Korea, Cuba, North-Vietnam and
Mongolia
Academia, Publishing House of the Czechoslovak Academy of Sciences
Prague

for all remaining areas
Elsevier Publishing Company
335 Jan Van Galenstraat, P.O. Box 211, Amsterdam, The Netherlands

LIBRARY OF CONGRESS CARD NUMBER 69-18140

STANDARD BOOK NUMBER 0-444-40965-3

WITH 155 ILLUSTRATIONS, 2 TABLES AND ONE MAP.

© Quido Zaruba, Vojtech Mencl 1969
Translation © H. Zarubova, V. Mencl

Printed in Cechoslovakia   Reprinted in The Netherlands 1972

PREFACE

Landslides are widespread in many countries and cause great economic losses, especially when engineering constructions are designed and erected without heeding the stability conditions of the slopes. The greater frequency of landslides provoked by construction works, as compared with the past, is probably due to several reasons. The interference with natural slopes is more intensive because of the rising boldness and extent of structures; the mechanization of earthworks accelerates excavation but excludes the possibility of sorting the rock material; the selection of building sites is generally restricted to the less favourable ones which were avoided by previous builders, etc.

The types of landslides are closely connected with the geological conditions of the area. The territory of Czechoslovakia, having a very intricate geological history, is the site of very diverse sliding phenomena. In 1962—1963 a survey of areas affected or threatened by sliding registered 9,164 landslides covering an area of almost 60,000 ha. Many of them endanger settlements, highroads, railway lines, canals and public utilities.

Therefore, we thought it desirable to sum up our knowledge of slope stability in a monograph that would provide information on the origin of slope movements, and the methods of their investigation, prevention and control. Numerous examples of landslides on Czechoslovak and foreign territories and of their treatment are referred to for a better understanding of this phenomenon.

We wish to express our thanks to Dr. L. Čepek and Dr. J. Kohoutek, who edited and revised this book, for their expert help and valuable comments.

February, 1967.   Q. Záruba, V. Mencl

CONTENTS

Chapter 1

INTRODUCTION

1.1 Definition of the term

The problem of the stability of slopes, both natural and excavated, has to be faced in many fields of human activity, particularly in civil engineering. When the slope stability is disturbed, sliding movements of most varied character take place.

Rapid movements of sliding rocks, separated from the underlying stationary part of the slope by a definite plane of separation, are designated as landslides in the stricter sense.

Sliding phenomena also include slow, long-term deformations of slopes which usually occur not along one distinct sliding surface, but within a thick zone consisting of a system of partial sliding planes. These deformations possess the character of a viscous movement and are termed the "creep".

Landslides and other slope movements have attracted the attention of man just as have other uncontrollable natural phenomena which threaten his life or property such as earthquakes, volcanic activity, etc. In some regions, landslides occur quite rarely, whereas in others they are so frequent that they represent an important factor in the modelling of the landscape forms. Because of the great damage they cause to forest growths, farmland, communications, engineering constructions and buildings, they may be a serious economic problem.

The sliding of slopes is not uncommonly caused by human activity, such as deforestation, incorrect construction procedure, etc. All the diversity of forms and intricacy of interrelationships, as well as the practical relevance of landslides, can be recognized only by systematic and thorough study.

Landslide phenomena are usually studied from two different points of view. As long as they are considered as a natural process co-acting in sculpturing the land surface, they are the subject of geological studies. Geologists study sliding phenomena as one of the significant exogenic denudation processes, with respect to the causes of their origin, their courses and the resulting surface forms. The approach of engineers and engineering geologists is quite different. They investigate the slopes from the point of view of the safety of the constructions to be erected on them. Therefore, they endeavour to ascertain in advance the proneness of slopes to sliding, to determine the maximum angle of excavated

1

slopes and to develop methods for a reliable assessment of the stability of slopes, as well as the controlling and corrective measures needed. The quantitative investigation of slope stability was evoked by the necessity to construct high fills and excavate deep cuttings for railways, highroads or canals. The disastrous landslides on the Swedish railroads provoked the establishment of a special Geotechnical Commission in 1914, whose studies laid the foundations for a new scientific branch—soil mechanics.

The best results of landslide studies can be achieved only by the combination of both these approaches. The quantitative determination of the stability of slopes by the methods of soil mechanics must be based on a knowledge of the geological structure of the area, the detailed composition and orientation of strata, and the geomorphological history of the land surface. On the other hand, geologists may obtain a clearer picture of the origin and character of sliding processes by checking their considerations against the results of static analyses and the research done by means of soil and rock mechanics.

From what has been said above, it follows that the study of sliding phenomena is of theoretical and practical importance both for the engineer and the geologist, as recognition of the causes, character and development of landslides makes it possible to appreciate the extent of the danger and to find an adequate solution for the control and correction of sliding areas. Landslides that are not anticipated or not well understood may endanger the results of human work and human lives.

1.2   Economic significance of landslides

To demonstrate the economic importance of landslides, the damage they can produce and some examples of their disastrous effects are listed below.

Landslides and slope movements may threaten:
(a) Single houses or entire settlements.
(b) Agricultural and forest lands.
(c) The operation of quarries and exploitation of mineral deposits.
(d) Communications under construction or in use.
(e) Tunnel constructions.
(f) Water, sewage, gas conduits, telephone and electrical lines.
(g) The functioning of submarine cables which may be interrupted due to subaqueous slides.
(h) Hydrotechnical works, particularly dam constructions.
(i) Diversion canals, penstocks.
(j) Reservoirs, contributing to their silting by material slid down of their banks.

The indirect adverse effects of sliding movements can be instanced by landslides which clog the valleys, thus impounding temporary lakes that endanger

2

the downstream reaches by flooding, or by the slides of shores generating dangerous waves in lakes or bays.

(a) In Europe, the Alpine countries have experienced many disastrous landslides and rockfalls, and numerous case histories have been referred to since Roman times. According to Heim (1932), in Switzerland alone more than five thousand people had lost their lives in landslide catastrophes.

One of the oldest historical reports describes a large rockfall which in 563 destroyed the community of Taurentunum on the bank of Lake Leman. The fallen rocks blocked up the Rhône valley, producing a large wave in the lake which devastated the banks (Heim and Buss, 1881). In 1584, a large landslip on the slope of Tour d'Ai above the Rhône valley wrecked the community Yvorne and more than 300 lives were lost (Heim, 1932). Also greatly damaging was the slide of Tertiary conglomerates on the slope of Rossberg, Switzerland in 1806, which destroyed the village of Goldau and took 457 lives (Fig. 1-1).

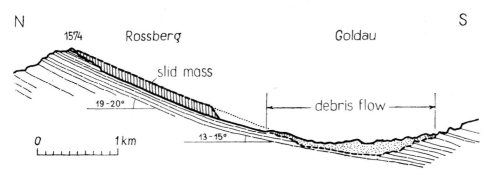

Fig. 1-1. Slide of Tertiary conglomerates along bedding planes, which in 1806 destroyed the township Goldau in Switzerland (from Heim, 1919).

The slides in the area of sensitive clays in Scandinavia and Canada often have tragic effects owing to the appalling suddenness of the motion. One of the largest landslides of this type occurred near Vaerdalen, north of Trondheim in Norway in 1893 (Holmsen, 1953). A layer of sensitive clay of marine origin was laid bare by the erosion of a stream. The liquefied clay, of a volume of 55 million m³, flowed down into the Vaerdalselven river-valley during 30 minutes. The dense liquid covered an area 8.5 km² large. The temporary lake created by the damming of the valley inundated 3.2 km². The disastrous landslide destroyed 22 farms and 111 persons were killed (Fig. 1-2).

A number of major landslides have occurred in America, of which the disastrous fall of Palaeozoic limestones from Turtle Mountain near the town of Frank, Canada in 1903 is an example. Within two minutes about 40 million cubic yards broke off, burying part of the town, an industrial plant and a long railway track, and taking at least 70 lives (McConnel and Brock, 1904). The landslides occurring in the Andes in South America, and in the Himalayas and the Pamirs have caused many still greater catastrophes.

On Czechoslovak territory landslides are not uncommon and have produced quite a bit of damage. A few of the major ones are briefly mentioned below.

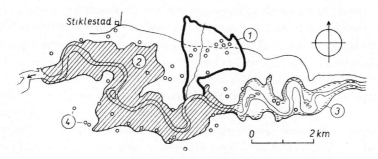

Fig. 1-2. Sketch map of the great landslip in Vaerdalen in 1893 (Holmsen 1953); 1 — head-scarp area, 2 — Vaerdalselven river-valley filled with liquid clay, 3 — temporary lake created by damming the valley, 4 — farms.

In 1820, the village Staré Stranné (the Žatec district, western Bohemia) was destroyed, including the church and schoolbuilding. The settlement was located on the slope of the river Ohře valley made up of Neogene clays. The movements

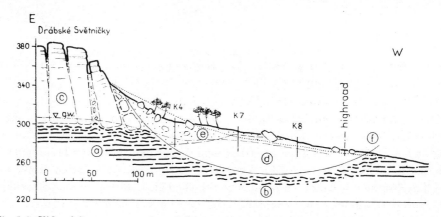

Fig. 1-3. Slide of Cretaceous marls and detritus at the foot of Mužský Hill in Bohemia in 1926; a — marls (Upper Turonian), b — moulded marls, c — sandstones (Senonian), d — slid moulded marls, e — slope debris, f — outcrop of the slip surface.

were repeated in 1872, 1882 and 1885 when the rock mass partly filled the stream bed (Křivanec, 1901).

On the slope of Hazmburk (north-western Bohemia), part of the village Klapy was damaged in 1882 and 1898—1900 by sliding basalt scree and Creta-

4

ceous marls (Woldřich, 1899; Stejskal, 1939). The movements were renewed in 1939. At the foot of Mužský Hill near Mnichovo Hradiště (north-eastern Bohemia), a large slide of sandstone debris and Cretaceous marls destroyed the village Dneboh in 1926 (Záruba, 1929a). In spring 1940, a major slide buried and wrecked the community Dolní Týnec in northern Bohemia (Keil, 1951).

Landslides are very frequent in Moravia and Slovakia, in the flysch regions of the Carpathian Mountains. In 1920 an earthflow near Hošťálková (eastern Moravia) damaged two villages; another one, near Dubková in the Lysá Pass, partly wrecked the Hlboká community (Záruba, 1938); a large slide near Riečnica in the Orava area in 1962 partly demolished three communities (Fig. 5-7).

Very serious in its effects was the landslide at Handlová in 1961, which ruined 150 houses (sect. 5.1.5), interrupted the highroad, water-supply conduit and high-tension electric line, and threatened the railway and the newly-built part of the town. All these landslides produced great damage, but thanks to the comparatively low rate of sliding movements, no lives were taken.

Fig. 1-4. Marginal blocks of a basalt flow (2) sunken into Cretaceous marls (1); (3) — debris. Quarry in north-western Bohemia.

(b) The depreciation of agricultural lands by sliding may also be extensive. The irregularly hummocky earth's surface and deep fissures aggravate cultivation and make the use of machinery impossible. In addition, the slope movements may cause unfavourable changes in soil conditions by removing the fertile upper layer, thus exposing the barren lower layers. Due to major disturbances, the land cannot be used even as pasture because the fissures, partly covered with vegetation, are dangerous both for people and cattle.

The economic damage caused by landslides in wooded areas may be very serious. The yield of forests may be decreased in terms of both the quantity and quality of the timber. The working and transport is likewise difficult owing to the disturbance of the terrain. Major slope movements result in the complete extirpation of forest growth and trees are uprooted or become dry. Afforestation on wetted clayey soils is very difficult and usually requires expensive drainage of the slide area and total recultivation.

The amount of damage to agricultural and forest lands in Czechoslovakia is

5

evidenced by the extent of the affected areas. The registration of landslides carried out in 1961—1962 recorded the following figures:

	Number of slides	Area in hectares
Bohemia and Moravia	4,792	30,264
Slovakia	4,372	29,136
total	9,164	59,400

Of this acreage, 35,000 hectares, or 59 per cent is agricultural land and 13,500 hectares, or 23 per cent is forest.[1]

(c) Landslides threaten and aggravate the work in quarries and loam pits. On the other hand, ill-founded and irresponsibly operated quarries may endanger the stability of the whole slope. Thus, for instance, the operation of basalt quarries in the České Středohoří Mts. is frequently difficult because of the sinking of marginal blocks into soft underlying rocks (Fig. 1-4). On opening the quarry in a sunken block, the floor should be gradually raised to a higher level.

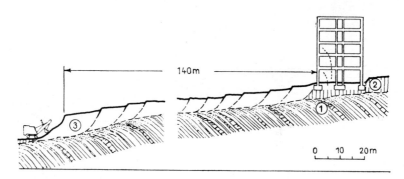

Fig. 1-5. Incorrect opening of a loam-pit at the toe of the slope provoked a landslide which threatened the stability of the building; 1 — argillaceous shales and sandstones of the Flysch Belt, 2 — slope loams and debris, 3 — loams and debris disturbed by sliding.

Great damage was caused by full-slope excavation in a loam pit in the Dřevnice valley (eastern Moravia). The undermining of the built-up slope resulted in the disturbance of stability; the progressive backward caving of the scarp threatened a public building standing 140 m from the original edge of the loam pit. Underpinning of the building and correction of the slope were necessary. The work in the brickyard had to be stopped. The damage brought about by reckless working procedure was increased by the depreciation of building-plots on the slope above the brickyard (Fig. 1-5).

---

[1] The extent of wooded areas affected by sliding is in fact still greater. Owing to the short period available for registration during 1961-1962, not all landslides, particularly those on not easily accessible mountain slopes, could be recorded.

Disastrous landslides are known to have been provoked by ill-founded quarries. Pits on talc schists opened on the slope of Monte Conto, N of Lago di Como promoted a rockfall that destroyed the town of Plurs and buried more than two thousand inhabitants (Heim, 1932). The well-known landslide in 1881 near Elm in the Swiss Alps was also caused by opening a quarry on roofing slates (Fig. 1-6). In a few minutes more than 10 million m³ of rock material slid down-

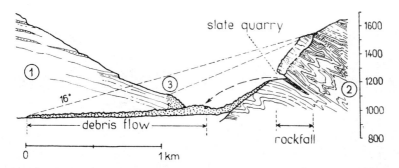

Fig. 1-6. The rockfall near Elm in Switzerland caused by the undercutting of a steep slope by a slate quarry (after Heim 1932); 1 — flysch sandstones and shales, 2 — Blattengrat Beds, 3 — debris pushed up the opposite slope.

ward filling the valley for an area of 90 ha to a height of 10 to 20 m. Eighty-three houses were demolished and 115 lives were taken (Heim and Buss, 1881).

(d) The highroads traversing the areas susceptible to sliding are not infrequently interrupted by landslides, either natural or artificial, if the stability of slopes was disturbed during their construction. Several examples of highroad failures are dealt with in Chapters 5 and 10. Landslides produce both direct and indirect damage; they threaten or even obstruct traffic and cause a considerable increase in maintenance costs.

Sliding movements create serious problems in railway construction and operation. The designer of the railway line across a potential slide area must avoid disturbing the slope stability by deep cuttings or high embankments; also, the construction procedure has often to be adapted to the unfavourable properties of the rocks. When the railway line is in operation, the trains should slow down in dangerous sections.

Permanent control and maintenance of the slopes is necessary. The performance of remedial measures sometimes even puts the line temporarily out of operation. The railway line on the seashore near Folkestone in England, for instance, has already been interrupted several times by landslips (Ward, 1945).

Cases are known when, owing to the permanent danger of slide movements demanding high maintenance costs, a railway line had to be relinquished. In Bohemia, the line Žabokliky—Březno (Žatec area) was discontinued after six years of existence (1873—1879). The traffic on this line, located on the valley side of the Ohře river, was too small to cover the cost of correction and maintenance measures.

Great damage to railway lines may be caused by slope movements in opencast mines (Fig. 1-7).

(e) Landslides also produce serious troubles in tunnel construction. The Unterstein tunnel near Salzburg was driven for the railway line in the Austrian

Fig. 1-7. A railway line interrupted by landslide; Brown-coal Basin Marica-Iztok in Bulgaria (photograph by Rybář).

Alps, in 1875 (Fig. 1-8). When the greater part of it had been lined and the last segments were being excavated, chloritic schists on the slope slipped down, causing the tunnel to cave in. The original line had to be abandoned and a new tunnel driven deeper into the mountain (Wagner, 1884).

A noteworthy failure occurred in New Zealand; a 175 m long railway tunnel, built in 1878, had to be abandoned and the route transferred in 1935 (Benson, 1940). The tunnel was constructed in Miocene sandstones superjacent to claystones dipping at 15° seawards. It has been ascertained that the tunnel crossed the upper part of a large landslide and was traversed by several cracks separating the individual displaced blocks (Fig. 1-9). Geodetic survey has shown that the blocks continued to settle and rotate so that the height position of the rails had to be continuously adjusted. In addition to these movements, gliding of the whole area has been revealed; its rate depending on the rainfall, amounted to 2—7 cm per month in the years preceding the dereliction of the tunnel.

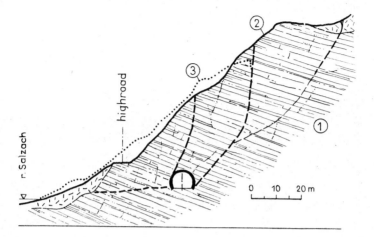

Fig. 1-8. Cross-section of the slid slope above the Unterstein tunnel in Austria, from Wagner (1884); 1 — chloritic schists, 2 — ground surface before the slope collapse, 3 — slope surface after the caving-in of the tunnel.

(f) Slope movements of different kinds have caused heavy losses to dam constructions. They occur mainly during excavation works. Thus, for instance, at the Grand Coulee Dam on the Columbia River in the U.S.A., the right abutment had to be stabilized during construction by freezing the young sediments moving downslope. The foundation excavations for the Fork Site Dam on the San Gabriel River in California promoted such a large rock slide along a fault zone in granite mass that the dam site had to be abandoned (Záruba, 1934).

In Slovakia, the stability of the valley slope was disturbed by excavating the foundation for the Dobšiná Dam. Fractured gabbrodiorite mass began to slide

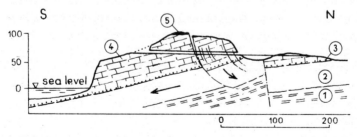

Fig. 1-9. Longitudinal section of the railway tunnel in New Zealand which was damaged by a landslide in 1935 (after Benson, 1940); 1 — glauconitic claystones (Upper Cretaceous), 2 — Tertiary claystones, 3 — glauconitic sands, 4 — crumbly sandstones, 5 — basalt.

9

on Carboniferous graphitic shales dipping 35° downslope (Fig. 1-10). Fortunately, the sliding was stopped by supporting the loosened rock upon completed dam segments by means of heavy frames, which made it possible to finish the dam construction.

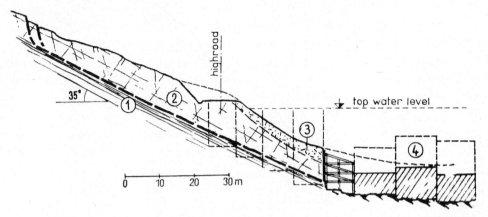

Fig. 1-10. Excavation for gravity dam abutment endangered the slope stability, central Slovakia; 1 — Carboniferous graphitic shales, 2 — gabbrodiorite, 3 — slope debris, 4 — concrete blocks under construction.

(g) The question of slope stability plays an important role in the construction of navigation and diversion canals. The building of canals often requires deep excavations which may promote extensive, very dangerous slides. Major landslides occurred, for instance, on the Panama Canal, in the Culebra cutting.

In Slovakia, slope sliding was a great drawback to the construction of the diversion canals on the river Váh; in some sections it determined the design of the whole work. Thus, for instance, the axis of the diversion canal between Krpeľany, Sučany, Lipovec (Záruba and Mencl, 1958) had to be modified because of deep-reaching landslides in Neogene sediments at the northern margin of the Turiec depression. The diversion canal near Mikšová on the Váh was also endangered by a fossil landslide revived by the excavating work (sect. 5.2.2).

Landslides and slope movements may also unfavourably affect penstocks and pressure conduits, feeding the water to power plants. Benson (1946) described such a case in New Zealand. The pressure conduit founded on a slope consisting of weathered and fresh chloritic schists, displayed deformations of anchoring blocks soon after the structure had been completed. As the deformation reached 10 cm in three months, the conduit had to be transferred from the slope surface into a gallery driven in solid rocks.

An ancient landslide caused severe troubles during the construction of the pressure tunnel for the Latschau power plant at Lünersee, in Austria. Water from the Lünersee reservoir should have been conducted to the power plant

10

by an inclined pressure tunnel. Geological survey, however, has shown that the slope above the power plant was disturbed by a Pleistocene landslide, so that a section of the conduit had to be placed on the slope surface for shortening the section built in the slid rock mass. The shape of the displaced block was assessed by a series of borings and exploration drifts (Fig. 1-11). In the opinion of Austrian geologists (Mignon, 1962), the movement took place after the retreat of a glacier when a voluminous complex of crystalline schists slipped along an ancient tectonic surface onto an old moraine at the foot of the slope. The driving of the pressure tunnel was extremely difficult in this section, especially at the base of the slid blocks where crushed Triassic sandstones and morainic deposits were encountered.

(h) Large landslides may block the mountain valleys and give rise to temporary impounded lakes. The "dams" formed of downslipped masses are not sufficiently firm; they generally collapse when first overtopped by water and cause disastrous floods. One of the largest catastrophes of this kind occurred in the southern Alps in the sixteenth century. In 1512 a rock slide of 150 million m³ dammed the Brenno valley near the township of Biasco creating a lake more than 50 m deep with about 200 million m³ of water. Two years later the dam collapsed

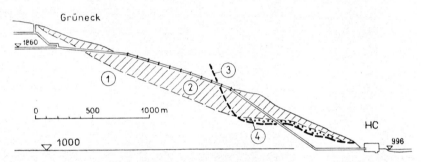

Fig. 1-11. Pleistocene landslide affected the location of the pressure gallery to the Latschau power station in the Austrian Alps; 1 — phyllites and chloritic schists, 2 — slid crystalline schists, 3 — shape of the glaciated valley before the landslide, 4 — morainic deposits (after Mignon, 1962).

and the flood caused heavy losses downstream and on the banks of Lago di Maggiore. According to historical data, more than 400 houses were destroyed and the loss in lives exceeded 600 (Heim, 1932).

A large temporary lake was caused by the blocking of the Rhine valley by an interglacial landslide near Flims. The lake level was at first more than 600 m above the valley bottom. The lake no longer exists, as the powerful stream deepened the valley again, almost to its original level (Fig. 1-12).

In the Pamirs, an enormous landslide took place in 1911. Downslipped rock mass, estimated at 4,800 million m³, filled the valley of the river Bartango, impounding a lake 75 m long and 260 m deep (Yakovlev, 1954). Extensive

Fig. 1-12. The Rhine valley cut in the limestone material of the interglacial landslide near Flims in Switzerland (photograph by Záruba).

12

landslides of this kind were also recorded in the Himalayas; in 1893 a temporary lake, 7 km long, was thus created on the upper Ganges. The following year the dam of downslipped material failed, causing a disastrous flood in the whole Ganges valley.

An analogous example was recorded in the Gros Ventre valley in Wyoming, U.S.A.; in 1925 the mountain slope slid along the bedding plane in Carboniferous claystones. About 38 million m³ of rock dammed the valley and a 60 m deep

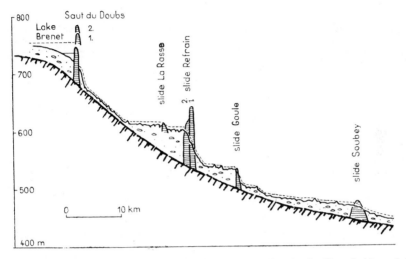

Fig. 1-13. Conspicuous steps in the long profile of the Doubs river in the French Alps originated by the damming of the valley by landslides (after Buxtorf, 1922).

lake formed upstream; the dam collapsed when the water overflowed its crest. In the drainage area of the Mantaro River in Peru, a rockfall created a dam more than 100 m high which broke after 73 days; the flood discharge was fifty times the annual discharge (Snow, 1964). When the dams built up of slid rock masses are sufficiently large and firm, permanent lakes may be formed. Thus, the lake Klönsee in the Glarn Alps was produced by a large interglacial landslide, the volume of which is estimated at 770 million m³. Davos Lake and a number of others were also impounded by a landslide.

Landslide-dammed lakes have been recognized in the Carpathian region also In 1828 the slide of a rock wall formed of Dogger limestones, east of Georgheni, Rumania, gave rise to the still existing lake called Lacul Rosu. As the flooded valley was overgrown by forests, numerous remains of trees protrude above the water level. The lake occurring in the Blatná valley, south of Lubochňa, Slovakia, was also generated by a large rockfall of dolomitic limestones.

Many dammed lakes were gradually silted, and alluvial deposits developed steps in the length profiles of watercourses. At some places these steps have been preserved; elsewhere, only remnants of lacustrine deposits were left on the slopes, the main aggradations having been removed by erosion. Either alternative is very unfavourable for dam foundation. The length profile of the Doubs river in France (Fig. 1-13) shows several conspicuous steps which were originated by the blocking of the valley by downslipped material (Buxtorf, 1922). The reaches, where gravels were aggraded on the valley bottom, do not provide

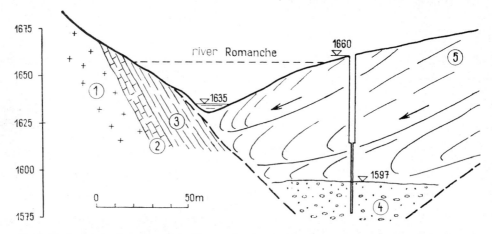

Fig. 1-14. A narrowed section of the Romanche river valley, considered as a potential dam site, is due to the accumulation of slipped Lias shales (5); 1 — granite, 2 — sandstones, 3 — Triassic limestones, 4 — sandy gravels of the ancient valley (from Gignoux and Barbier, 1955).

very good conditions for the construction of dams. On the upper Romanche, upstream of the Chambon Dam in the French Alps, the dam site originally selected seemed to be topographically suitable. Geological survey, however, showed that the valley was blocked by a landslide (Fig. 1-14), and the river bed raised by 40 m and shifted towards the left side. The Liassic complex of pelitic shales was not in situ, but slipped on permeable river deposits of the ancient valley. Thanks to timely recognition of these unfavourable circumstances, the dam site was abandoned (Gignoux and Barbier, 1955).

On the Ticino river in the Tessin canton, Switzerland, a steep step in the length profile also proved to be produced by a large rockfall (Nägeli, 1920). Between the townships Giornico and Lavorago the Ticino river flows five kilometres through a narrow gorge formed of huge blocks of Tessin gneiss (Figs. 1-15 and 1-16). In this section the stream gradient is 240 m, whereas up and downstream of the gorge, where the river-plain is more than 500 m wide, it is only 12 m/km. Two to three rockfalls of 500 million m³ occurred after the retreat of the glacier, thus causing the overdeepening of the valley and disturbing the stability of orthogneiss dipping 30—35° downslope on the left bank. The remains of lacustrine alluvia on the valley slopes point to the

14

existence of a temporary lake due to the damming of the valley. Headward erosion proceeds comparatively slowly through the slid mass, as this consists of large blocks of solid orthogneiss, many of them being larger than 5,000 m³. This steep step in the thalweg caused great difficulties in designing the Gotthard railway line in this section. The height difference of 240 m had to be overcome by two loop tunnels driven through orthogneiss deep in the undisturbed slope.

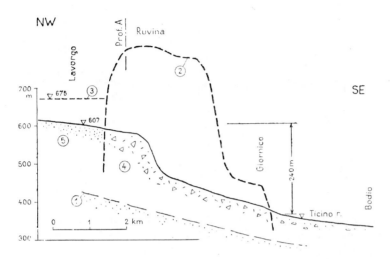

Fig. 1-15. A sector of steep gradient in the long profile of the Ticino river, caused by the filling of the valley by a rockfall; 1 — the height of alluvium before rockfall, 2 — the highest accumulation of slid orthogneiss in the valley, 3 — height of impounded water in the temporary lake; 4 — rockfall material, 5 — lake deposits (modified after Nägeli, 1920).

(i) Sudden landslides of sea shores have very disastrous indirect effects. In Norwegian fiords, landslides often provoke high swells of up to several tens of metres which threaten the inhabited coast. In 1936 a rockfall, 1 million m³ large, near Loen, produced a 74 m high swell in the Nordfjord; in this catastrophe 73 lives were taken (Bjerrum and Jörstad, 1966).

One of the largest slide-caused disasters known so far occurred in the Vaiont reservoir in the Italian Alps in 1963. A complex of Jurassic and Cretaceous limestones of about 260 million m³, slid suddenly from the slope of mount Toc into the reservoir impounded by the 265 m high dam. The mass abruptly filled the greater part of the reservoir, causing a water wave higher than 100 m which overflowed the crest of the dam, destroyed the township Longarone, and damaged other communities in the Adige valley. Almost 2,000 people lost their lives (Selli et al., 1964).

A series of dangerous slides originated as a result of lowering the level of some Alpine lakes after their incorporation into the new hydro-electric schemes. During the construction of the Davos-Klosters dam in Switzerland, for example,

15

the lowering of the Davos Lake level by 11 m (Moor, 1923) triggered a slide of 900,000 m³ of material of an alluvial cone. The abrupt movement of such an enormous mass provoked a tempestuous surge which broke an ice cover 80 cm thick on the lake into small floes, and caused heavy losses on the shores.

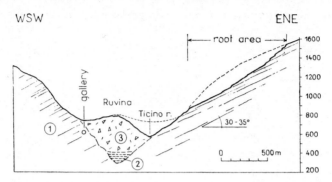

Fig. 1-16. Cross-section of the narrowed valley of the Ticino river at the site of rockfall; 1 — Tessin orthogneiss, 2 — old valley sediments, 3 — fallen orthogneiss blocks (after Nägeli, 1920).

The artificial lowering of the level of Lake Spullersee in the Tyrol, likewise resulted in the downslipping of banks in sections formed of pelitic sediments and deltaic deposits at the mouths of brooks.

The length of life of some reservoirs is shortened due to the sliding of banks which contributes to their rapid silting. This is especially characteristic of valleys whose slopes are disturbed by ancient landslides or are susceptible to sliding, as is the case in some Alpine or Carpathian regions.

The above are only a few examples of how slope movements have influenced the geomorphological history of the earth's surface and what their manifestations are today. Although many others could still be cited, these sufficiently demonstrate the economic importance of sliding processes and how they can endanger buildings and civil engineering works, as well as communication and water structures, when the liability of the area to sliding has not been recognized or has been ignored.

Chapter 2

THE DEVELOPMENT OF LANDSLIDES FROM THE POINT OF VIEW OF SOIL AND ROCK MECHANICS

2.1   General aspects

Statical solutions of soil and rock masses have attained a satisfactory level of perfection and some of them, e.g. the investigation of the settlement of constructions, have proved to be a competent aid to designers. Yet, statical analyses of the stability of slopes are as a rule more difficult and less reliable for several reasons:

(a) Problems of stability are much more affected by both the anisotropy and non-homogeneity of the mass than are deformation analyses. Consequently, the correctness of the results depends much more on the ability of the investigator to give a true picture of the geological setting of the site in relation to the mechanical properties of rocks. As the geological structure of natural slopes is generally complex, the statical solution deals with a rather idealized picture of the real slope and the adequacy of this picture is of importance.

(b) Several factors act simultaneously. Therefore a good theoretical knowledge is necessary in order to assess correctly the true decisive factors. Ground water percolating towards the surface of the slope is generally one of the most important factors.

(c) The safety factor of those slopes that are usually subjected to investigation, is generally smaller than 1.5. Under these conditions the straining of the material is so large that the statical solution of the theory of elasticity cannot be applied. On the other hand, when dealing with foundations of structures the standard factor of safety is generally larger than two and consequently the elastic solutions give a good picture of the state of stress. But since the volume of the sliding mass also changes, not even the standard theory of plasticity can yield realistic statical solutions of landslides.

(d) The denudation and erosion of natural slopes and excavations for railroads, etc. result in a reduction of weight and in a decompression of material. As a result, the strength and deformation parameters develop in a different way than when under compression and, as a rule, deteriorate with time.

(e) Rainwater, frost and other climatic agents attack the slopes. If the statical solutions of the stability of slopes are to present realistic results, an understanding of the behaviour of the soil and rock is necessary. Only a knowledge of all factors, of their changes as well as of their influence upon the slope, can avoid the danger of a stereotyped solution.

The subsequent paragraphs do not claim to analyse the mechanism of all kinds of slope deformation and slide movements as they will be treated in Chapters. 4 and 5 together with geological features. They are rather a discussion of several factors of a statical character in order to recognize their fundamental bearing on the development of landslides. In this respect three factors deserve attention: the mobilization of the resistance of soil and rock masses with increasing deformation of the slope (sect. 2.2); the influence of the state of stress upon the development of slope failures (sect. 2.3); and the presence of water in the slope (sect. 2.4).

2.2 The influence of the mobilization of shearing resistance upon the development of slope failures

(a) Two items will be discussed: the deformation due to shearing forces and the formation of a slip surface. There is no doubt that the stress field in a slope (Fig. 2-1) is characterized by large shearing stress components, since the difference between the two principal stresses is large. Along the directions

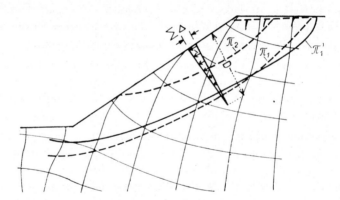

Fig. 2-1. Directions of the main stresses within the slope (thin lines), curves of maximum shear stresses (π_1, π_2) and the true slip surface π_1'. Prior to the origin of the slip surface, the slope deforms; in the section demarcated on the slope edge the deformation value is $\Sigma\Delta$.

of the surfaces π_1, π_2, etc. the mass deforms by shearing. However, unless the shearing stress is high enough to give rise to slip surfaces, the soil or rock mass deforms in its full thickness, without exhibiting abrupt slip deformation. With dense clayey soils this is up to a shearing displacement of about 2.5 cm per one metre-distance of surfaces π_1, π_2, etc. (Mencl, 1966a). It follows, for example, that with a thickness of a sheared body D of about 6 m, a total settlement of the top of the slope equal to about 15 cm can be assumed.

18

Since the slope surface in the upper parts is usually rather stiff, cracks appear. These cracks need not be considered as a demonstration of a loss of stability. Yet, they reveal that it is small, smaller than about 1.3, and that they can often give rise to a landslide, if for example, rainwater should get in. With compact rocks this limit is smaller; with stiff shales or claystone it is about 8 mm per one metre.

If deformation exceeds the given values, we may conclude that the slip surface develops. But the volume of the dense soils or compact rocks increases along the slip surface. With dense clayey soils it results in augmentation of the water content by approximately a few per cent and in reduction of the shear resistance. The increase in volume influences the shape of the slip surface, because it results not only from maximum shear stress but is also controlled by normal stress, which resists the increase in volume. This bends the slip surface and its cross-section is rather the shape of a logarithmic spiral than of a circle. Instead of the surface π_1 one obtains the surface π_1' (Fig. 2-1).

With dense sands or gravels this increase in volume is relatively large (about 5 to 8 per cent) and therefore the slip surface develops near the surface where the normal stress is small, and with the exception of a short head scarp, it is nearly straight. Exceptions to this rule are slope failures in a cohesionless soil mass, when the shape of the slip surface is predetermined by the failure of underlying clayey soil.

In loose soils and rocks or dense soils or rocks at large depths the increase in volume does not occur and a distinct slip surface does not develop at all. The mass deforms in its full thickness up to the failure. For instance, Mencl (1966b) has reported that with Cretaceous sandstone this occurs beginning with a pressure of about 500 to 600 kp/cm².

A special category is represented by failures along surfaces which have existed in the mass prior to its exposure to shear forces. These surfaces are, for example, bedding planes and therefore can have any shape. If the curvature of the surface changes, the slip movement can be either triggered or hindered, which may influence the stability of the slope (sect. 2.2.c).

(b) The strength of soils and rocks and its changes during the development of a landslide are worthy of mention. Although specialists in engineering geology are familiar with fundamental questions of the shear strength of rocks and soils, certain features merit discussion:

The full mobilization of shear resistance in soils and rocks, as in other materials, is associated with a displacement. The deformation-stress diagram (Fig. 2-2) of a shear test illustrates this fact. With small dimensions of shear test apparatuses, differences in displacements Δf can be observed. The displacements change from one to three millimetres with the value of normal stress. When computing the safety factor of a slope, in which the slip surface cuts several kinds of rocks or soils, great attention is paid to the problem of pro-

19

gressive failure, which is associated with the fact that the peak value of the resistance is not achieved in different materials simultaneously. However, field shear tests on large blocks (dimensions of about 80 cm) present less distinct displacements necessary to achieve peak values. With the exception of rigid rocks on the one hand, and weak soils on the other, they are about

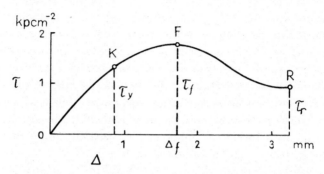

Fig. 2-2. Diagram of shear test on hard clayey soil; Δ — displacement of clamps, τ — shear stress, τ_y — yield limit, τ_f — strength limit, Δf — displacement at strength limit τ_f.

7 to 9 mm. The smaller relative difference as compared with laboratory tests is caused by the fact that the more resistant the material, the larger the tangential stress in the block and therefore its deformation is not due solely to yielding along the slip surface. The deformation of the adjacent mass helps to decrease the displacement along the shear surface in a stiff mass and to increase it in a weak one.

The successive mobilization of shear resistance and progressive failure must often be considered when dealing with rocks. Unless a large tangential displacement develops, weak layers (e.g. filling of fissures) do not exhibit the peak value of resistance. On the other hand, rigid jags are subjected to a concentrated stress and break with small displacements. Consequently, it is not easy to solve the stability of rock slopes and the factor of progressive failure is very important.

In soils the progressive mobilization of strength appears with backward-breaking head scarps, as shown in Fig. 2-6a.

The second problem, observed less by engineering geologists, is associated with the fact that tangential stress also increases the stress level in the body. Let us assume that the original state of stress at a certain point of the mass is represented by Mohr's circle K_1 (Fig. 2-3). If a tangential stress is added (e.g. by increasing it from τ_1 to τ_2), the stress level corresponds to a new circle K_2 which, in the Mohr diagram, is shifted to the right, i.e. towards larger σ, as compared with K_1. Therefore, the volume of material is reduced. But in clays or clay shales this reduction is associated with a consolidation process, which is relatively slow, often slower than the increase in shear stress. This holds true, for example,

20

for the toes of natural slopes which have been suddenly subjected to oblique pressures caused by a soil mass sliding from the upper sections of the slope. Soil mechanics approaches this problem by distinguishing the strength under total consolidation from that which appears with the so-called consolidated-quick tests. The rate of loading during the test is adapted. In the former case both the normal and tangential stresses are increased very slowly. The angle of shear stress (φ_d') is about 20 degrees with clay and about 25 degrees with loam (line D' in Fig. 2-3). On the other hand, if consolidated-quick tests are applied, the soil is subjected to a slow consolidation by normal stress and afterwards the tangential stress

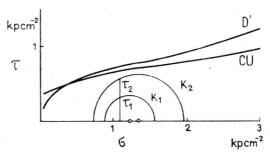

Fig. 2-3. The change of Mohr's circle (from K_1 to K_2) with the increase of shear stress; D' — strength curve of the clayey soil after full consolidation produced by pressure σ and shear, CU — strength curve after consolidation by pressure, but at an abrupt increase in shear (without consolidation).

is increased rapidly. The resulting strength is smaller, the angle of strength (denoted either by φ_{cq} or φ_{cu}) amounts to only 16 to 20 degrees (line CU in Fig. 2-3).

When analyzing the stability of a slope, attention must be paid to distinguishing which of the two parameters is to be applied. Also the course of excavation work should be considered; the slow progress of excavation, as was common in times of manual work, was more favourable for consolidation in the course of excavation than the rapid mechanized operation of today. But with the latter, too, the consolidation (under tangential stress) can be controlled by an adequate schedule of excavation.

The third item relates to the development of stress in clays or claystones. By excavation the soil is relieved of the weight of the removed mass; as a result, the effective stress is reduced e.g. from σ_a' to σ_b' (Fig. 2-4). The line of strength D' of the relieved material is curved; in the domain of σ' larger than about 0.5 kp/cm², a portion of precompression remains in the material. But this does not hold true for smaller σ', to the left of point c. Consequently, the line is curved, a fact that is often disregarded when testing the strength. Then the strength line is defined, for example, by points a and c and the parameters of the straight line D" are obtained. In the domain of small σ', as it develops after the excavation has finished, the line D' bends downwards. Therefore, especially with low slopes, the stability can be much smaller than follows from the statical analysis.

(c) Another problem is the influence of the shape of the slip surface on the mobilization of the soil or rock resistance. No important changes in shape occur in the rock mass moving along a circular surface (Fig. 2-5a). Small changes occur during the first deformations. Therefore, the stiffness of the mass has no influence upon the stability. This probably holds true also for landslides arising

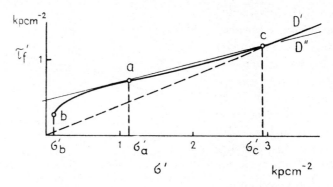

Fig. 2-4. Strength curve of a preconsolidated clayey soil; σ_c' — preconsolidated by the overlying beds, already removed by erosion, σ_a' — pressure of present overburden, σ_b' — presure after the excavation of the cutting.

along slip surfaces with curvature decreasing downwards (sect. 2.2.a), irrespective of the distinction that the tensile stress and hence small resistance against failure exists near the head scarp.

On the other hand, the stiffness of the sliding mass is of great importance with landslides along slip surface exhibiting an increase of curvature in their lower sections (Fig. 2-5c). This is the case of landslides having a predisposed slip surface, e.g., along bedding planes. The sliding mass should either deform or break (Fig. 2-5c) in the course of sliding and therefore, its stiffness interferes with the ultimate limit equilibrium analysis. Secondary crosswise slip surfaces often develop with landslides of this category.

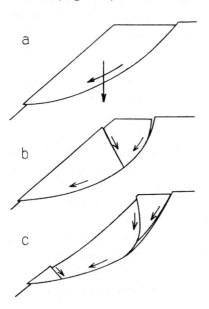

Fig. 2-5. Mechanism of the landslide movement on slip surfaces of different curvature; a — circular slip surface, b — slip surface having the form of approx. logarithmic spiral, c — compound slip surface.

2.3 The influence of the state of stress upon the development of slope failures

The importance of the changes in the resistance of rocks and soils, in the progress of a landslide has been discussed in the preceding sections. In the present one, attention is drawn to another factor. The natural state of stress in earth masses is often characterized by large horizontal stresses, which exceed the vertical stress several times. This state probably results either from the position of the site with respect to the general tectonic structure of the area, or is a remnant of the stress field which existed before the area has been laid bare by denudation, or is connected with large fossil landslides. Some values have been given by Mencl (1962b, 1965b). When excavating or in the course of valley erosion, these stresses give rise to several kinds of deformations:

(a) Horizontal forces transferred through the mass concentrate in the bottom of a cutting or a valley after the mass is removed. Therefore, horizontal stresses increase in the mass under the bottom, exceeding its strength and a system of slip surfaces develops in the bottom and in the slopes near the toe (Mencl, 1955, 1965a). A characteristic feature is the disappearance of such a slip surface into the slope at a short distance, e.g. within 4 — 5 m in cuttings of the usual dimensions. The existence of these slip surfaces need not invalidate the stability of slopes, unless they open by shrinkage and are penetrated by rainwater. Nevertheless, they are a sign that the mass is deforming and that the safety factor of the slope is smaller than about 1.2.

(b) As the mass of the lower layers deforms towards the open space of the cutting or valley, tensile cracks originate near the top of the slope and in adjacent areas. The mass carries along the overlying layers, in which either horizontal pressure does not exist at all (e.g., Quaternary sediments lying on the bedrock of Tertiary claystones) or has been reduced by subaerial agents (weathering, temperature changes, desiccation). Instead of exhibiting cracks, the plastic or fissured mass often becomes loosened, and its porosity increases.

Surface water or subsurface water penetrates deep into the cracks. Therefore, landslides of the upper section of the slope occur soon after the cutting has been excavated. On the other hand, deep slides reaching up to the bottom of the excavation follow after several months, when the relieved mass near the toe has bulged (sect. 2.2.b). This development in stages is characteristic.

(c) Another specific feature of this category of landslides is a partially backward movement. While with landslides in general, after the development of the first crack (denoted by 1 in Fig. 2-6a) the other cracks appear higher and higher (cracks 2 and 3, a retrogressive landslide), the mechanism of the given category of landslides has an opposite character: the first crack appears far from the edge of the cutting (1 in Fig. 2-6b) and the following cracks (2 to 4) successively approach the edge. The relative movement of the blocks is therefore backwards, compared with the general displacement towards the cutting. However, retrogressive failures also appear after the slope (Fig. 2-6c) has collapsed. The outcrops of backward slip surfaces of old stabilized landslides are indistinct, whereas the recent slumps of the slope give them a resemblance to retrogressive landslides.

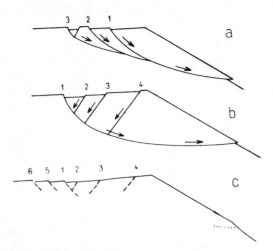

Although the design of preventive measures will be discussed in Chapter 8, the need for timely detection of this type of landslide should be emphasized. However, statical solutions are not easy, mainly because the problem of locating the potential first crack has not yet been solved. Another difficulty is that this type of landslide develops in areas with subhorizontal surfaces, and that it appears despite the fact that the results of the classical stability analysis may have been on the safe side. An example of a landslide of this category is the collapse of the cutting near Bánovce (Chapter 8).

Fig. 2-6. Normal and backwards movement mechanism of landslides; a — normal retrogressive landslide, b — landslide with backward slip surfaces, c — backward movements on surfaces 2, 3, 4 in a dormant landslide obliterated by retrogressive movements along surfaces 5 and 6.

2.4   The influence of ground water

The forces exhibited by the seepage of water through the soil mass are known. Uplift is another well-known detrimental factor respected in statical solution. But it is necessary to be fully aware of the potential unfavourable effects of these forces upon the slope. These effects differ from those implied by simply introducing the resulting forces into the statical solution. In particular the following aspects should be recognized:

(a) In stiff homogeneous clays, forces caused by seepage give rise to slip surfaces which are located deeper than is usual. This is due to the reduction of the effective normal stresses caused by seepage or uplift forces. It facilitates the increase in volume along the slip surface (sect. 2.2.1), even if the weight of the overburden is large. Slip surfaces in the form of logarithmic spirals arise. With them the stability is smaller by several per cent (7 per cent, in Mencl, 1966a) than if a circular surface is analysed.

24

(b) Water flows out of the slope near the toe and the mass is softened and begins to slake. Often the collapse of a slope extends from a small disturbance upwards and sidewards. This phenomenon should be kept in mind when testing soils. The specimens should be subjected to a similar loading system; it is not sufficient to respect the seepage as a statical factor only and simply to decrease the normal pressure. Kenney (1961) discussed the fact that under effective stresses σ', that are equal but result from different total stresses σ, and from different pore water pressure u, (since $\sigma' = \sigma - u$), the parameters of strength may differ one from another. Therefore, it is better if the actual magnitudes of σ and u (and σ', of course) are modelled in the laboratory.

(c) Many sheet landslides have a similar character except that the first failure does not begin at the toe of the slope, but at the point where water flows out. Subsequently, blocks of soil move and new blocks cover the issue of water, preventing its free escape while the material is softened. Rainwater participates, too.

(d) Landslides which originate when a large uplift operates on the contact of the lower, more permeable layers with the overlying less permeable ones, are characterized by a rapid spreading of the collapsed area. In a few hours new cracks set wide apart and the terrain surface indicates that blocks of large areal extent have originated, although the inclination of the slope is relatively small.

2.5   Viscous flow

Weak pelitic soils exhibit the first signs of viscous flow with loading equal to about half the short-time strength. They do not increase in volume when sheared and, consequently, no distinct slip surfaces originate. Because of a low Bingham limit (the magnitude of the stress up to which the deformation has a retarding character), they behave as viscous materials. The largest displacements occur at the surface and diminish with depth. Therefore, no definite slip surface limiting the slide body exists; one may speak rather of a boundary between the moving and stationary mass. Consequently, even if the curvature of the slip surface does not change, the mass deforms. The first cracks are much larger than stated in sect. 2.2a. In Neogene clays of the Carpathian Foredeep the first signs of this process appear with a water content of about 30 %. The mass deforms like a drop and changes into an earthflow (Chapter 5). The collapse is always of a progressive character and extends either downwards (on slopes with a gradient of about 10 degrees) or by retrogressive slumping, if the slope gradients are smaller or if the landslide is initiated by erosion or excavation near the toe.

Chapter 3

FACTORS PRODUCING SLIDE MOVEMENTS

To recognize the reasons for the susceptibility of an area to sliding, and the factors which trigger the movement of the rock mass, is of extreme importance, because only a precise and correct diagnosis can serve as a basis for effective remedial measures. The variety of landslide types reflects the diversity of factors which are responsible for their origin. They are briefly characterized in the following paragraphs:

1. The change of slope gradient. This may be due to natural or artificial interference, i.e. to the undermining of the foot of the slope by stream erosion or by excavation. Exceptionally, the change of slope gradient may be produced by tectonic processes, by subsidence or uplift. The increase in slope gradient provokes a change of stress in the rock mass; the equilibrium is then disturbed by the increase in shear stress. Upon the relief of lateral stress the rocks on the slope loosen and facilitate the penetration of water.

2. *The excess load by embankments, fills and waste dumps.* The overloading may lead to an increase in shear stress and in the pore-water pressure of clayey rocks, which in turn produces a decrease in strength. The more rapid the loading, the more dangerous it is.

3. *Shocks and vibrations.* Earthquakes, large-scale explosions and vibrations of machines produce oscillations of different frequencies in rocks, and thus a temporary change of stress which can disturb the equilibrium state of the slope. In loess and loose sands, shocks can cause a disturbance of intergranular bonds and consequently, a decrease in cohesion or internal friction. In saturated fine sands and sensitive clays, shocks may result in a displacement or rotation of grains leading to a sudden liquefaction of the soil.

4. *Changes in water content*

(a) The effects of precipitation. Rain and melt water penetrate into the joints producing hydrostatic pressure; the increase in the pore-water pressure in soils induces a change of consistence, which in turn causes a decrease of cohesion and internal friction. Recurrent sliding movements generally occur in the years of unusually high rainfall.

(b) Some authors who have measured the difference in electrical potential between two beds on the contact of which a sliding plane was formed, explain the increase in the water content inducing slope movements as due to electro-osmotic processes.

(c) In periods of drought clayey soils desiccate and shrink; as a result of this, fissures open, the cohesion of the soil diminishes and water can penetrate into the clayey rocks.

(d) Abrupt changes of water level (e.g. along the banks of reservoirs) may induce a displacement of grains, especially in fine or silty sand. A sudden increase in pore water pressure may result in a sudden liquefaction of soil.

5. *Effects of ground water*

(a) Ground water flow exerts pressure on soil particles, which impairs the stability of slopes.

(b) Ground water can wash out soluble cement and thus weaken the intergranular bonds; consequently, cohesion decreases and the coefficient of internal friction drops.

(c) The moving ground water washes out fine sand and silt particles from the slope and the underground cavities thus formed weaken the stability.

(d) Confined ground water acts on the overlying impervious beds as uplift.

6. *Frost effects.* The freezing water in rock fissures increases in volume, which results in a widening of existing fissures and the formation of new ones and consequently, in a decrease of the cohesion of rock. In clayey and clayey-sandy soils, ice laminae are formed which, on melting, enlarge the water content in the surface layer.

7. *Weathering of rocks.* Mechanical and chemical weathering gradually disturbs the cohesion of rocks. There are indications that in some landslides, chemical changes (hydration, ion-exchange in clays) induced by percolating water, are another deleterious factor. Thus, for instance, areas built up of clays and glauconitic sandstones show a susceptibility to sliding.

8. *Changes in the vegetation cover of slopes.* The roots of trees maintain the stability of slopes by mechanical effects and contribute to the drying of slopes by absorbing part of the ground water. The deforestation of slopes impairs the water regime in the surface layers.

3.1   Dependence of slope movements on the amount of precipitation

In view of the recurrence of slope movements in extremely humid years, it seems reasonable to study the influence of the amount of rainfall on the activation of movements in individual sliding areas.

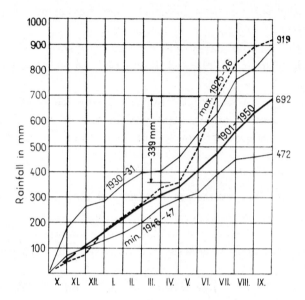

Fig. 3-1. Summation lines of monthly rainfall computed for several years, based on the observation of the State Hydrometeorological Institute; data from the Turnov area in Bohemia.

The diagram (Fig. 3-1) of monthly rainfall totals for the Turnov area, compiled from the data of the State Hydrometeorological Institute (Záruba et al., 1966) may serve as an example. The mean rainfall in the 1901—1950 period, i.e. for fifty years, was 692 mm. In 1926, when the rainfall reached the maximum of 919 mm, the large landslide near Dneboh and many others developed. A decisive factor in their origin were the spring rains amounting to 339 mm, which is the two-month maximum recorded during seventy years of ombrometric measurement.

The interrelationship between the rainfall and the frequency of landslides is even clearer from Fig. 3-2 showing successive three-year averages of precipitation from 1879 to 1935, which are based on records of the ombrometric stations at Louny, Střemy and Česká Lípa. In the Cretaceous region of Bohemia, the successive three-year average values show very clearly the influence of climatic conditions on the height of the ground-water table, as the ground-water system is affected by the precipitation of the two preceding years (Záruba, 1936). The most humid three-year intervals (see diagram) of 1899—1901, 1914—1916

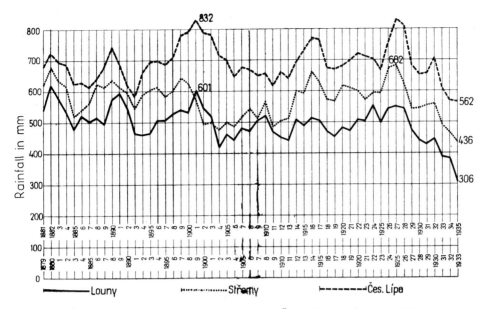

Fig. 3-2. Three-year averages of rainfall for stations Česká Lípa, Louny and Střemy. At the periods of maximum rainfall a revival of landslides is presumable, (from Záruba, 1936).

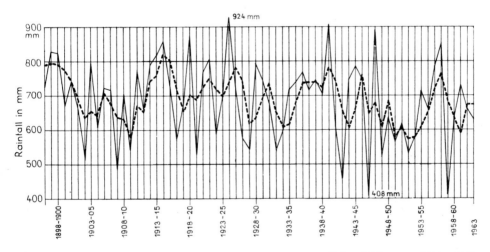

Fig. 3-3. Annual rainfall amounts for the Turnov area (northern Bohemia) between 1898—1963; dashed line — computed three-year averages.

and 1925—1927 correspond to the periods of most intensive slope movements in the Cretaceous region (Hazmburk, Klapý, Podmokly, Dneboh, Přerov n. L., etc.). On the other hand, in the driest interval of 1933—1935 many structures were damaged owing to the desiccation and shrinkage of Cretaceous marlstones on which they were founded.

Figure 3-3 lists successive three-year mean values of precipitation for the Turnov (from 1898 to 1926) and Karlovice (from 1926 to 1963) ombrometric stations. In the diagram, annual rainfall means are also plotted, beginning with November 1 of the preceding year. The most humid periods in the Turnov area were also 1897—1899, 1898—1900, 1914—1916, 1925—1927 and additionally 1939—1941. Maximum rainfalls were recorded in 1926 and 1941, when numerous landslides also occurred.

A systematic examination of ombrometric records makes it possible to predict the renewal of slope movements in the areas liable to recurrent sliding, and to warn of imminent danger, especially, to public communications.

Chapter 4

DIVISION OF SLIDING PHENOMENA

Sliding phenomena involve such a variety of processes and disturbing factors that they afford unlimited possibilities of classification. They can be divided, for instance, according to the form of sliding surfaces, to the kind of material moved, to the age or rate of movement, or the stage of development.

Of the authors who proposed a classification of slope movements, let us name, at least, Heim (1882), Howe (1909), Almagia (1910), Terzaghi (1925), Ladd (1935), Sharpe (1938), Emelyanova (1952) and Varnes (1958). From the engineering-geological point of view, Terzaghi's division of landslides based on physical properties of the rocks involved, had many advantages. Sharpe (1938) classified the sliding movements with regard to the material of moving mass, to the type and rate of movement, and studied the relations of mass movements to the geomorphologic cycles and climatic factors. An analogous division has been proposed by Varnes (1958) and adopted by the Landslide Committee Highway Research Board (Eckel 1958). Most of these classifications are best applicable to particular regions, as they are obviously influenced by the conditions of the area where the respective author carried out his studies.

In Soviet literature the division of Savarenskii (1937) is frequently used. This author uses the shape of the sliding surface as the distinctive feature and distinguishes asequent, consequent and insequent landslides.

Asequent landslides develop in homogeneous cohesive soils. The movements take place along curved, roughly cylindrical surfaces.

Consequent landslides occur along bedding planes or other planes of separation inclined downslope (joints, schistosity planes and the like). The slipping of slope deposits on the bedrock surface is involved in this group.

Insequent landslides run across bedding and usually attain large dimensions; the sliding surfaces generally extend deep into the slope. Deep-reaching landslides on concave valley sides or on the seashore (e.g. near Odessa or at Folkestone in England), are designated as insequent.

In Popov's (1951) opinion, the landslide classification should also take regional conditions into consideration, which, owing to a diversity of controlling factors, modify the individual landslide types. Such a classification would enable a more precise characterization of sliding movements and provide a safer basis for remedial measures.

For Czechoslovak territory and for the purposes of engineering geology, we regard as most convenient such a division of slope movements that takes into consideration regional geological conditions, and enables a sliding phenomenon to be classed within a group on the basis of simple characteristics, easily determinable in the field. As the predominant part of landslides concerns the Pleistocene superficial deposits, they are assigned to a separate group, which is further subdivided according to the type of movement. The classification of the sliding movements of bedrock is based on the character of the rocks involved and on the type of movement.

Using these principles we put forward the following scheme:

A. Slope movements of superficial deposits (slope loams, debris) due mainly to subaerial agencies:
    (a) Creep of debris which also produces the bending of strata.
    (b) Sheet slides.
    (c) Earth flows.
    (d) Debris flows (Muren, liquefaction of sands).

B. Slides in pelitic, unconsolidated or partly consolidated rocks (clays, marls, claystones, pelitic shales), developed:
    (a) On cylindrical surfaces, when the shear resistance is exceeded,
    (b) On predisposed surfaces, on ancient planes of separation,
    (c) By squeezing out of soft underlying rocks (including sliding of fills caused by the same process).

C. Slope movements of solid rocks:
    (a) Slides on predisposed surfaces (bedding, schistosity, jointing or dislocation planes).
    (b) Long-term deformations of mountain slopes.
    (c) Rockfalls.

D. Special kinds of slope movements which under the present climatic conditions do not occur in Czechoslovakia but are elsewhere an important geological process:
    (a) Solifluction.
    (b) Slides in sensitive clays (quickclays).
    (c) Subaqueous slides.

4.1   Geological development of landslides and their age

Sliding phenomena are due to the activity of many factors, among which the time factor also plays an important role. As the individual agents change in the course of time, the slide passes through several phases of development. At first, the stage is set for the origin of a landslide, the first signs of the disturbance of equilibrium appear and cracks in the upper part of the slope develop; afterwards the loosened mass is propelled into motion, slides downslope and is gradually deposited. By the accumulation of slid masses Nature alone creates temporary equilibrium conditions.

According to their development, the slides can be divided into initial, advanced and exhausted landslides (with the root area quite emptied).

On the basis of the degree of stabilization, active, dormant and stabilized slides may be distinguished. According to age, they are divided into contemporary and fossil; the latter cannot revive under the present-day climatic and morphological conditions.

Contemporary (generally active) landslides are relatively easily recognizable by their configuration, because the surface forms produced by the mass movements are expressive, being not effaced by rainwash and erosion. Trees are diverted from their original position; roads and alleys traversing the sliding areas are interrupted and buildings are often damaged and deformed. The slopes may be moving or set into motion at any moment, because of the existence of slide-provoking factors.

Dormant landslides are usually covered by vegetation or disturbed by erosion so that the traces of their last movements are not easily discernible. The causes of their origin, however, remain, so that the movement may be renewed. A dormant slide can occur, for instance, on a concave bank of a river which, having temporarily shifted its channel, stops undercutting an ancient slide.

Fossil landslides generally developed in the Pleistocene or earlier periods, under different morphological and climatic conditions and cannot repeat themselves at present. A dormant landslide whose origin was described in the foregoing paragraph, may turn into a fossil one when, for example, the river after shifting its channel recommences vertical erosion, so that the old flood plain becomes a terrace. When such a slide is covered by loess loams or other young deposits it is termed a buried landslide.

Chapter 5

GEOLOGICAL DEFINITION OF THE MAIN LANDSLIDE TYPES

5.1   Slope movements of surface deposits

This group comprises slope movements developed in the surface layers and conditioned by the activity of subaerial agents, by the character of slope deposits and the topography of the slopes.

5.1.1   Creep of debris. The creep of debris is a slow, up-to-imperceptible movement of rock fragments downslope, resulting from diverse processes. During the winter months it is facilitated by the loosening of rock fragments and the upheaval of surface layers by frost. On thawing in spring, the particles do not fall back to their original position but under the influence of gravity shift slightly downhill. The movement of loose stone debris downslope is mainly due to temperature changes (expansion by heat and shrinkage on cooling).

The clayey surface layers move slowly downhill by the action of long-term plastic deformation. These movements, designated as creep, do not usually develop a discrete slide surface but a shattered zone, within which many minute partial movements take place. They are confined to the surface layer, not reaching below the depth of temperature and humidity effects. The deformations need not exceed a few millimetres annually but during geological periods they appear as a continuous creep of slope deposits.

The creep of slope debris was studied by Haefeli (1944) who compared it with plastic deformations occurring in a snow bed on a mountain slope. In both cases,

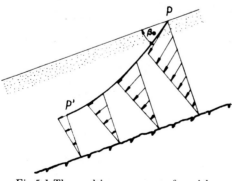

a slow movement valleywards is combined with the vertical movement of particles (subsidence). The rate of movement is highest near to the surface, decreasing towards the substratum. Simultaneously, the density of the snow increases, which is converted to firn and finally to ice, unless the stability degree is surpassed and the snow bed falls downslope in the form of an avalanche (Fig. 5-1). Slope deposits likewise undergo a compaction which, however, proceeds at a much lower rate.

Fig. 5-1. The resulting movement of particles at the creep of slope detritus (after Haefeli, 1944).

5.1.2 **Bending of beds.** The creep of the surface layer of debris and weathering material results in the bending of beds. Friction active between the creeping debris and the surface of the bedrock, produces a gradual bending of outcropping faces of beds regardless of their dip (down or upslope). The dragged-out and disrupted layers of the bedrock become part of slope deposits, thus increasing their thickness.

Originally, the bending of beds was interpreted in terms of glacial activity. This assumption led to an erroneous opinion on the extent of the ice-sheet in Central Europe. Later, on the basis of Götzinger's observations (1907) from the flysch area of the Northern Alps, it was regarded as a recent phenomenon. However, the Palaeogene flysch complexes, particularly when weathered, are

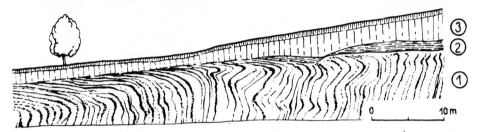

Fig. 5-2. Surface bending of beds in a loam-pit in Prague (loc. "Pod Andělkou"). 1 — Ordovician shales, 2 — Cenomanian claystones, 3 — loess loams.

so susceptible to sliding, even under the present climatic conditions, that the findings ascertained there cannot be generalized for areas built up of more stable rocks. In the Carpathian flysch regions the presence of ancient, definitely fossil landslides has been ascertained so that it cannot be decided to what extent the terminal bending of strata dates from the Pleistocene, and to what extent it originates in recent times.

It is now almost generally believed that the dragging out and bending of strata on the gentle slopes could not develop under the present climatic conditions, i.e. that these phenomena originated in the periglacial climate during glacial periods. Intensive physical weathering gave rise to voluminous scree which was redeposited during summer thawing by solifluction even on low-angle slopes. After the weathered surface rocks had been removed, the outcrops of solid beds were involved in the regelation zone and disturbed by recurrent freeze-and-thaw to such a degree that they could be dragged downslope.

The terminal bending of strata is widely distributed on slopes made up of shales, thin-bedded sandstone or limestone, gneiss, quartzite, shattered granite, etc. In the surroundings of Prague, conspicuous terminal bending of the Devonian limestone beds is observable in abandoned quarries at Žvahov; the bending of the Ordovician shales could be seen until recently in an old brickyard at Střešovice (Fig. 5-2).

The terminal bending of strata is also of practical significance, as it can interfere with the excavation works due to the fact that the rocks tend to slip along the upper surfaces of the dragged-out beds. In the foundation pit on the northern slope of the Motol valley, weathered Ordovican shales drawn-out by solifluction were encountered beneath slope debris and loess loams at a depth

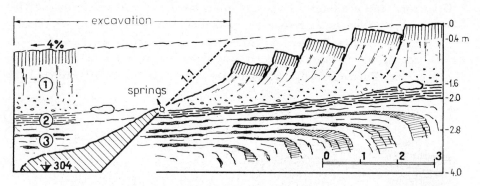

Fig. 5-3. A system of ancient slip surfaces in the dragged-out Ordovician shales was interrupted by an excavation, and slope failure followed; 1 — slope loams and debris, 2 — dragged-out Cenomanian clays, 3 — weathered Ordovician shales.

of three metres below the ground surface. Ancient slide planes on the surface of the bedrock were disrupted by excavation and the slope above them moved down. Although the angle of the slope was only 4°—6°, the disturbance extended high above the excavation and required expensive corrective treatment (Fig. 5-3).

A note for less experienced geologists: care must be taken not to measure the strike and dip of beds affected by bending instead of beds in their natural position, as may happen, for instance, in shallow test pits.

5.1.3 Sheet slides. The term sheet slides is used to denote the movements of shallow slope debris, loams and weathering materials on the surface of the bedrock. The surface layers showing this type of slope movements are usually at the most two to three metres thick, but may cover extensive areas in some regions. On the disturbed slopes, various stages of sliding are observable from the initial movements, manifested by the opening of fissures, up to advanced forms with several generations piled on top of one another. Sheet slides extend gradually upslope. The steep head scarp is stable only in dry weather; after heavy rainfall or spring thaw the disturbance of the slope continues upwards.

The movement of sheet slides is invariably renewed at the spring thaw, particularly after a long frosty spell. During the freezing of the ground, the surface layers of clayey-sandy and loamy debris are enriched by water rising by capillarity towards the surface from the lower unfrozen beds. The water

Fig. 5-4. A sheet slide in slope debris near Žatec in western Bohemia (photograph by Záruba).

freezes progressively, forming thin ice laminae which, on thawing, cause the slaking of the surface layer.

Where clayey or marly rocks crop out on the slope surface, sheet slides develop by the slipping of weathered pelitic rocks along the unweathered bedrock. The weathered beds are frequently disrupted into small blocks separated by deep desiccation cracks formed by the shrinkage of clay. As a result of alternating drying and swelling, the blocks become separated from the unweathered substratum. The fissures generally end sharply at the contact of the weathered and unweathered zone and because they are filled with rainwater, the weathered rocks are under hydrostatic pressure. In addition, the rainwater soaking into the soil lubricates the bed below the irregular prismatic blocks of the still solid soil. The swelling of the blocks along the fissures produces considerable horizontal forces that give rise at first to a characteristic undulation of the slope surface and finally to slide movements.

Sheet slides of this origin are frequent in those parts of the Cretaceous basin of Bohemia where clayey or marly rocks are exposed, and in the Neogene sediments of north-western Bohemia (Žatec area, Fig. 5-4) and of Moravia

37

(north of Hranice, between Ostrava and Karviná, etc.). They are a current phenomenon in the Carpathian flysch regions in eastern Moravia and Slovakia.

This type of sliding may be instanced by the landslide on the Chlomek ridge at Ctiměřice near Mladá Boleslav. The landslide occurred in 1926, a year extremely rich in rainfall; the consistence of weathered sandy marls was disturbed by water of several springs issuing from the overlying weathered sandstones (Fig. 5-5). The excavation carried out in the loess loam at the toe of the slope

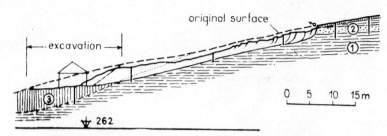

Fig. 5-5. Section through a sheet slide at Ctiměřice near Mladá Boleslav; 1 — Upper Turonian marls, 2 — Upper Turonian sandstone, 3 — loess loams.

acted as an additional factor. Water-logged marls slipped down and destroyed two buildings. Since 1926 the slope has been virtually at rest, the scarp has been levelled by ploughing and the fissures are almost imperceptible.

An analogous sheet slide took place at Přerov nad Labem in the same year. The lower part of the slope of the Bílá hora hillock is composed of soft marl, whereas the elevation itself is made up of solid flaggy marlstone of the Lower Turonian age (Fig. 5-6). At the foot of the slope there is a 2 to 4 m thick layer of marly slope debris. The sandy marlstones are jointed and permeable and a marked horizon of ground water accumulates on the surface of the underlying impermeable marls. The beds dip gently (4° to 6°) to NNE, and at their contact on the northern slope, a number of springs rises. The increased discharge of

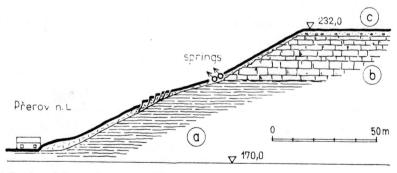

Fig. 5-6. Section of the northern slope of Bílá Hora near Přerov n. Labem: a — Turonian marls, b — flaggy sandy marls, c — Pleistocene terrace (Záruba, 1926).

springs at the time of heavy rainfall motivates the movement of slope detritus. According to written records, slope movements were observed at this locality in 1882 and 1899. The most intensive slide movement in 1926 demolished nine buildings. It is of interest that the years of sliding were also richest in rainfall over a period of 55 years, as is seen from the following table.

Year	Rainfall in mm	Percentage of the average
1882—1883	719	127 %
1899—1900	779	136 %
1925—1926	906	158 %
average		
1879—1926	570	100 %
minimum		
1904—1905	393	68 %

In 1926, sheet slides were observed at many other places: near Mladá Boleslav within the area of the Chlomek ridge; in the Jičín area, as well as in the Kladno district, where forest land was largely disturbed. At the latter locality the rampart of a prehistoric hill fort was also damaged. From such an extensive occurrence of sheet slides in one year it may be inferred that there is a connection between their origin and the amount of rainfall, i.e. that high precipitation is a decisive factor promoting the movement.

5.1.4 **Earthflows.** This type of landslide usually occurs in the same areas as the sheet slides but under particular topographical conditions. The shape of an earthflow adapts itself to the relief of the ground surface, its position being predetermined by an erosion gully or stream valley. Earthflows generally head in a large basin in the upper part of the slope where slope debris and weathering material is accumulated. Heavy rainfall may trigger the movement of this loose mass which, in the form of a narrow flow, travels towards the foot of the slope forming there a loaf-shaped bulge. Compared with sheet slides, they move at a greater rate because water-saturated debris packed into a narrow tongue contacts the substratum over a smaller area and consequently, the friction is smaller. Moreover, earthflows develop on steeper slopes where the movement energy of sliding mass co-acts in the movement. When all loose material is emptied from the root area, the landslide becomes gradually stabilized and overgrown with vegetation. If, however, part of the debris remains there, heavy rainfall may cause further movements and the old bulge at the toe is overridden by the younger material.

Earthflows with a high-lying root area filled with slope debris are always a serious hindrance to all engineering works, especially communications, as the remedial measures on mountain slopes are difficult and expensive.

Earthflows often originate in gullies predisposed by layers of soft or tectonically disturbed rocks. In the Carpathian regions, the Flysch Belt and the Pa-

Fig. 5-7. Earthflow near Riečnica, Orava, 1962, as an example of typical debris slides in the Carpathian flysch (photograph by Rybář).

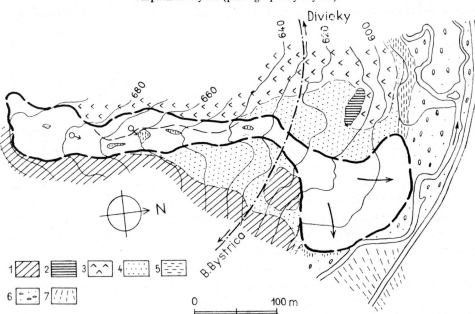

Fig. 5-8. Earthflow in the Žarnovice valley on the Banská Bystrica—Diviaky railway line. 1 — Triassic dolomite, 2 — andesite, 3 — andesite tuffs, 4 — slope loams and debris, 5 — marsh, 6 — sandy gravels, 7 — alluvial cone.

40

laeogene complexes of the Klippen Belt (in the Orava and Váh valleys) furnish most favourable conditions for the development of large earthflows; in the Keuper argillaceous shales they are somewhat scarcer.

Fig. 5-8 shows an earthflow in the valley of the Žarnovice streamlet. It was studied in detail as it had to be traversed by the railway line Banská Bystrica-Diviaky (Záruba and Andrusov, 1936). The earthflow developed in an erosion furrow running between Triassic dolomites and andesite agglomerates. The root area lies about 100 m above the valley. In the test-pits argillaceous shales of

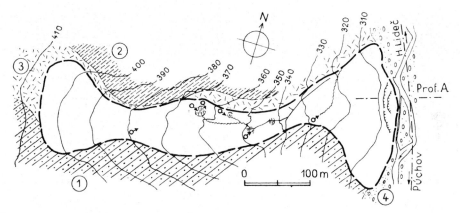

Fig. 5-9. Earthflow at Dohňany near Púchov (Slovakia); 1 — Marly limestones (Neocomian), 2 — argillaceous shales (Palaeogene), 3 — slope debris, 4 — sandy gravels.

the Keuper hidden below a thick layer of slope debris were encountered. Clayey waste and weathered tuff agglomerates moved as a narrow flow towards the foot of the slope, where they formed a wide loaf-shaped tongue. The presence of argillaceous shales was obviously an important factor in provoking a fairly large landslide in an area where slope movements on the whole are a scarce phenomenon.

The accumulated mass lies on the valley bottom on sandy gravels of the Žarnovice streamlet. On account of this position, it was well drained so that the tongue did not spread outwards. Later movement changed only the relief of the flow, as additional material was heaped upon the older in form of bulges and ridges. The railway line traverses the landslide on an embankment and the slide area had been stabilized by a system of drainage trenches which discharged surface and ground water.

The railway line from Púchov to Horní Lideč was constructed in an area formed of rocks susceptible to sliding. The earthflow near Dohňany (shown in Fig. 5-9) fills an old erosion gully developed between Palaeogene argillaceous shales and Lower Cretaceous (Neocomian) marly limestones. The contact of these two complexes is tectonic and the position of the erosion gully is controlled by a small resistance of tectonically disturbed rocks to erosion. During the

41

period of heavy rainfall the waste material got saturated, lost its stability and in a stream-like form flowed valleywards. The mass accumulated on gravel alluvia of the floodplain of the Biela voda stream. The root area, lying in a wide depression about 110 m above the valley, is filled with slope debris which, in the southern part, is composed mainly of fragmentary Neocomian limestones

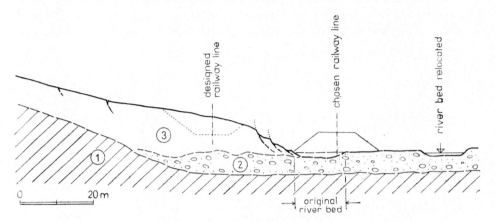

Fig. 5-10. Section A of the area of accumulation, landslide near Dohňany; 1 — Palaeogene shales, 2 — sandy gravels, 3 — slid clayey debris.

and marls, and in the northern part, of argillaceous shales and sandstones of Palaeogene age. During the railway construction the ancient landslide was not yet stabilized, because its equilibrium state was, from time to time, disturbed due to the undermining of the toe by the river at high water level. Natural levees fringing the middle part of the flow are a conspicuous topographical feature.

The railway-line was originally designed in a cutting which would encroach upon the slide tongue and thus very probably disturb the stability of flow. Therefore, it was relocated on a four metre-high embankment, erected on sandy gravels of the flood-plain (Fig. 5-10). Water, flowing from the root area and yielded by springs and wet grounds at the northern margin of the slide, was discharged by drainage trenches. The undercutting of the slide tongue was stopped by relocating the stream channel; the railway embankment also contributed to the stabilization of the flow. No movement have been observed since 1937.

5.1.5 **Earthflow near Handlová.** One of the largest slides in Czechoslovakia occurred near Handlová in Slovakia in 1960. Using this landslide as an example, the development of earthflows, research methods and corrective treatment will herein be discussed in detail.

In 1960 the slopes near Handlová were disturbed by extensive movements which destroyed part of the town and caused considerable economic losses.

42

The main slope movements show the character of the earthflow and produced large deformations of the ground at the foot of the slope.

The earthflow I (Fig. 5-11) originated in December 1960 on the eastern valley slope of the Handlovka streamlet in a shallow gully filled with slope

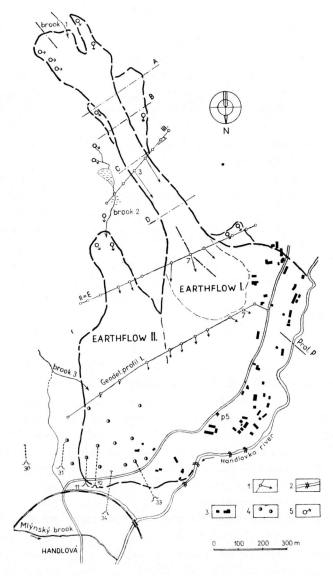

Fig. 5-11. Situation of earthflows near Handlová in 1960-61; 1 — vectors of points surveyed from January 1 to May 31, 1961; 2 — rubble work barriers in the Handlovka bed; 3 — destroyed buildings; 4 — hydrogeological borings from which water was pumped by means of submersible pumps; 5 — large springs in the root area.

debris. From the topography of the slope above the present root area and from air photographs taken in 1955, it was apparent that it had been the site of past sliding. The movement involved debris of volcanic rocks and clayey and silty sediments of Sarmatian age which had already been entrained downslope by previous movements.

Subsequent movement occurred in the upper part of the furrow, where a wide root area developed. The rock debris and weathering material accumulated there were saturated by surface and issuing ground water, and flowed in the form of a narrow stream valleywards. In the first phase of movement a bulge of slushed material about 300 m broad and 18—25 m high extended almost to the highroad. The great load of accumulated masses disturbed the equilibrium of voluminous slope debris piled at the base of the slope which resulted in the movement of the area in front of the toe of the earthflow. This additional sliding accounts for an unusual widening of the flow at the base (from 80 to 110 m in the upper part of the slope up to 800 m and, combined with the adjacent earth flow II, to 1,200 m at the toe). The channel of the Handlovka streamlet was blocked by downslipped material in several sections and the water level was raised by 5—8 m. The water was impounded to form several minor lakes.

Before the earthflow in 1960 the root area was filled with about 15 m of debris and weathering material. During the movement, it was partly emptied so that in the spring of 1961 the thickness of its fill was only about 7 m; the thickness of mass moving in the earthflow reached 10—18 m and in the tongue area 20—25 m. The length of earthflow I totalled 1,800 m and the volume of moving rocks was as much as 14.5 million m³.

Earthflow II set into motion a fortnight later, at the beginning of January 1961, on the eastern side of earthflow I (Fig. 5-11). The root area of earthflow II developed in the contiguous furrow filled with slope debris of similar composition to that of earthflow I. The movements also affected the steep crest to the east, which is formed of andesitic debris and appeared to be stable. During the spring months of 1961, deep cracks developed on this crest, transecting it diagonally into marked steps. The course of the cracks suggested deep-reaching loosening of the rocks at the foot of the slope. Earthflow II is about 1 km long and about 130 m broad in the upper part and 400 m at the toe. The volume of the sliding mass was roughly 5.7 million m³, so that altogether more than 20 million m³ of rocks were moving.

Geological background. —The basal part of the slope affected by sliding is built up of Palaeogene pelitic shales and sandstone interbeds in flysch development. They are overlain by the Neogene complex with Tortonian coarse-grained tuffites at the base and the Handlová coal-seam formation. The coal seams thin out eastwards so that their thickness is quite reduced on the sliding slope. Higher up, there are weakly consolidated clay-sandy sediments, particularly grey and greyish-green clays, and silts with intercalations of fine-grained

44

sands. This Tortonian sequence is followed by the so-called Sarmatian Gravel Formation composed of sandy gravels and clays. The top part of the slope is built up of thick sheets of andesite and andesite agglomerate.

The steep marginal rock walls of the volcanic sheets suffered from subsidence movements which took place mainly in the Pleistocene as a result of the squeezing out of plastic substratum. The margins of sheets were broken into large blocks which sank into lubricated pelitic rocks and moved valleywards. Isolated andesite and agglomerate blocks torn off the originally continuous volcanic sheets and scattered over the slopes of the Handlovka valley, furnish evidence of these ancient movements (Fig. 10—19).

The sinking and slipping of marginal blocks occurred simultaneously with the downcutting of the Handlovka river, which contributed to the unloading of soft Neogene sediments and, consequently, to their gradual squeezing out by heavy blocks of volcanic rocks. The consistency of Neogene pelitic sediments at the time of these deformations is not sufficiently known. It cannot reliably be said whether the difference in loading was sufficient to cause the squeezing out of underlying clays, or whether the change in clay consistency by periglacial climatic effects was the co-acting factor. As no contemporaneous movements of the marginal blocks are observable, the latter case seems to be more probable.

In places, the foot of the steep rock wall is covered by thick talus sheets. Andesitic debris slipped progressively downslope and mixed with weathered Tertiary rocks, so that the debris deposits form an almost persistent layer, 10—20 m in thickness. Clayey beds alternate haphazardly with sandy loams and coarse stony debris of andesite and andesite agglomerate.

Causes of slope movements. — In the Handlovka depression the geological and topographical conditions are extremely favourable for the origin of slope movements. In the upper part of slopes, the mode of deposition of the Neogene rocks impair the stability conditions; plastic pelitic sediments are overlain by heavy volcanic rocks divided into large blocks by joints at the margin of the sheet.

The susceptibility to sliding is also increased by the composition of inhomogeneous slope sediments, which in some places are permeable, composed of sand and rock fragments, whereas in others, clay beds predominate. Both Neogene sediments and weathered pelitic shales are disturbed and dragged out by ancient slope movements. New movements develop mostly on previous slide planes within surface layers of Palaeogene shales whose physical and chemical properties facilitate sliding.

Topographical conditions are an important factor which largely control the course and extent of landslides. The slopes formed of semi-consolidated clayey sediments would have been readjusted to a lower gradient long ago, if their upper edges had not been protected from denudation by sheets of solid volcanic rocks. The juvenile relief of the Handlová depression is also influenced by young tectonic movements manifested by the subsidence of the area in the lower reach of the Handlovka river which, as a consequence, has a steep and ungraded slope. The transportation power of the river is another contributive factor as it is great enough to remove the slipped-down rock mass. The undercutting of the foot of the slope disturbs the stability of debris deposited in the lower part of the slope, especially in those reaches where steep concave banks develop.

No less important are hydrogeological conditions. The alternation of permeable and impermeable rocks throughout the slope is responsible for the existence of several overlying ground water horizons, viz. in the jointed volcanic rocks above the impermeable clays, in the Sarmatian gravel and sand deposits and in the weathered surface layers of Palaeogene age. Impersistent pervious layers of waterlogged debris alternate with clayey soils in slope deposits also. Spring water issuing at the base of jointed volcanics, seeps together with the rainwater into slope debris, changing its consistency and impairing its physical properties. In addition, in the period of heavy rainfall, uplift is effective in permeable beds with a less permeable roof and decreases friction on slide surfaces.

The immediate cause of slide movement in 1960 was a large increase of water inflow into ancient slide masses, due to unusually high precipitation. According to observation of the ombrometric stations in Handlová and Prievidza, the precipitation of that year surpassed the mean value of 1901—1960 by nearly 50 per cent, the major portion of it falling into the autumn and winter months. According to the data of the ombrometric station the fifty years' average was 689 mm, while in 1960 the rainfall in the Handlová area amounted to 1,045 mm.

Moreover, the old drainage works being used for a more rapid discharge of surface waters were neglected, so that, for example, brook 3 (Fig. 5-11) which drained a quite extensive area to the east of earthflow II, discharged its water into the peripheral crack of this slide. One of the first corrective measures was concerned with the transfer of stream water back to the original channel. The seepage of water had also increased in recent years because the slopes, deteriorated by fly-ash, could no longer serve as pasture land and their ploughing disturbed the grass cover.

Reconnaissance and corrective works. — The results of the landslide just mentioned were disastrous; 150 houses were demolished, the main water supply and electrical conduits were destroyed and the Handlová—Žiar n. H. highroad was disrupted. Immediately after the slope failure, geological research and corrective works were begun. At first, the progressive extension of the landslide and deformations of threatened buildings were carefully observed so that rescue and evacuation work might be organized in time.

The systematic measurement of the rate of movement started on December 22, 1960, i.e. about 10 days after the first indication of sliding appeared in the root

46

area. In the slide area nine geodetic profiles and a chain of points along the high-road were established. Movements were checked every fourth day and the chain every other day. In Fig. 5-11, several of these profiles are plotted and the movement of individual points between January and the end of May 1961 is indi-

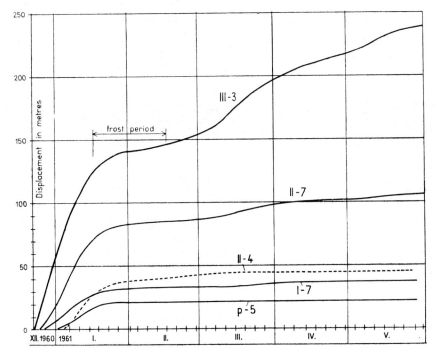

Fig. 5-12. The rate of movement of several points in profiles I, II, III, between December 1960 and May 31, 1961 (after Bajtoš, 1961).

cated. The largest horizontal shift (240 m) was measured in profile 3, in the middle part of the earthflow. In the area of deposition, horizontal displacements were of minor amount (106 m in profile II and 38 m in profile I). Maximum horizontal shifts measured in the chain amounted to 22 m (Bajtoš, 1961).

In the first days the movement rate of the earthflow was as high as 6.30 m in 24 hours (in profile III). The rate gradually decreased (Fig. 5-12) during long freezing, and in the summer months of 1961 the movement ceased completely. Although the rate of sliding was considerable during the first days, it was possible to organize the evacuation of threatened buildings so that there were no casualties or losses of lives. The houses were at first cracked and collapsed after only two or three days.

Measurement of transverse profiles. The nature of the landslide is clearly seen from the profiles measured and geologically appraised in April 1961. The profiles were chosen so that the original ground surface and the probable course

47

of the slide could be reconstructed. The highest surface of accumulated sludge
was inferred from the height of the preserved lateral ridges. The analysis of the position of the cracks and the individual blocks made it possible to differentiate
in the profiles between the main earthflow and subsidiary lateral flows, which
developed gradually on either side of the root area, and in places where the ancient valley was deepened by erosive effects of the earthflow.

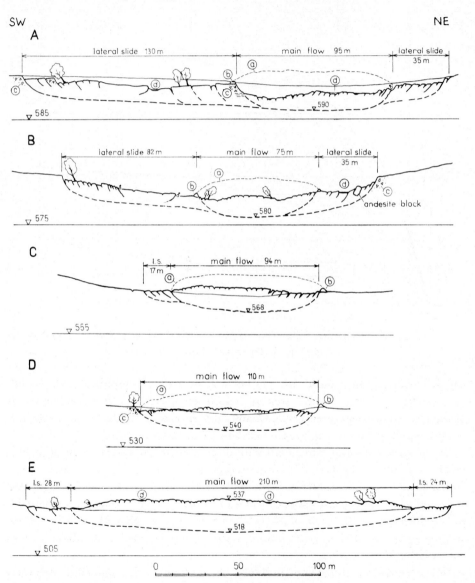

Fig. 5-13. Cross-sections of earthflow I near Handlová; a — the highest level of the earthflow, b — squeezed out ridges, c — andesite debris, d — lakes on the slide surface.

Profile A (Fig. 5-13) is drawn across the slide, about 380 m from the upper edge of the root area. The main earthflow 95 m wide is bounded there by definite longitudinal cracks. The highest level of accumulation reached el. point 613 towards the end of December 1960, as evidenced by the lateral ridge heaped up at the left margin of the earthflow. In April 1961 the root area was emptied considerably and the surface of the flow dropped by 12 m. In the left side of the scar, loamy-sandy debris with andesite blocks above slickensided greenish-grey clays of Sarmatian age were found. Towards the end of March and at the beginning of April 1961 several lateral slides originated which extended the root area by 130 m on the left side and by 35 m on the right side; the width of the root area in profile A totals 260 m.

Profile B (Fig. 5-13) was surveyed across the earthflow, 110 m below the profile A. The main 75 m-broad earthflow is distinctly limited by several longitudinal cracks filled with water-saturated clay. The shape of the lateral ridge preserved at the left margin indicates that the slipped mass reached the elevation point 604 towards the end of December 1960.

The earthflow followed an old gully which in this section is moderately arched to the west. As a result, the earthflow is asymmetrical; the moving mass accumulated at the right side where a high sheer wall limited the slide. In April, the surface of the earthflow was substantially lower because most of the material already reached the foot of the slope. After the deepening of the gully, the slide progressively spread laterally, by 82 m on the left side and by 35 m on the right. In the steep scarp of the root area a block of agglomeratic tuffs with andesite boulders was exposed on the right.

Profile C (Fig. 5-13) was surveyed 170 m below profile B, the profile line coinciding with geodetic profile III. The main 94 m-broad earthflow was distinctly limited by a system of slip surfaces along which the rocks were liquefied. In January 1961, the earthflow rose about 12 m above the adjacent surface. On its outer side the clays were vertically striated owing to transverse basculation of the slide body. On the left side, raised blocks of fen overgrown with horsetail (Equisetum fluviatile) were observable. A lateral, about 17 m-broad slide developed only to the left of the main earthflow. The surface of the main earthflow was moderately uparched so that brooks discharging the root area flowed down the furrows on either side of the earthflow.

Profile D was drawn across the slide, 240 m below profile C. The width of the flow was 110 m and its margins were sunk below the original level of the terrain in April 1961. Lateral ridges up to 3 m high, preserved on the right side indicate the maximum height of the moving mass which, towards the end of 1960, was approximately 23 m above the slide plane. At the surface, the flow is broken into irregular blocks which at the margin are aligned into longitudinal waves. The middle part of the flow is moderately bulged. The water streams were confined to the marginal cracks, along which the rocks were lubricated.

49

Profile E was surveyed in the line of geodetic profile II in the upper part of the area of deposition, where the masses accumulated to a height of 8—10 m above the original ground surface. The width of the flow was 210 m; on either side there are lateral slides dragged down by the huge mass of the main flow.

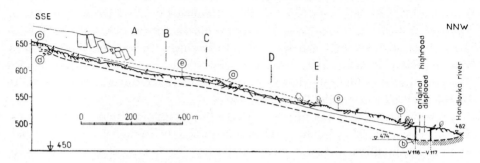

Fig. 5-14. Longitudinal section of earthflow I near Handlová; a — the highest level of the earthflow, b — marly shales (Palaeogene), c — slope debris, d — sandy gravels with interbeds of clay and tuffites, e — lakes on the slide surface.

Longitudinal profile I (Fig. 5-14) was drawn roughly through the centre of the root area and the earthflow as far as the cross-profile E. In these places the longitudinal profile was bent so as to run perpendicular to the Handlovka valley. Consequently, the length of the earthflow is 1,630 m in the surveyed profile.

The length of the root area is approximately	460 m
The length of the earthflow	600 m
The length of the area of deposition	570 m
Total length	1,630 m

Before the movements of 1960—1961 the gradient of the slope was relatively moderate. In the root area, up to profile B, the gradient is 12.6%; between profiles B and E it declines to 10.6%. The section between profile E and the highroad slopes at a minimum angle of 7.2%. Therefore, the downslipped masses accumulated in this section and at their toe subsidiary slides moved down, blocking locally the Handlovka channel.

The borings V-116 and V-117 sunk in the earthflow I, about 30 m above and below the highroad, revealed that the river valley had originally been deeper, being gradually filled by sliding material which pushed the stream channel towards the left bank. In 1960 the level of the Handlovka was about 12 m higher than the deepest level indicated by sandy gravels encountered in the borings. This would account for the ungraded slope of the stream in this reach. The displacement of the channel to the left bank resulted in increased lateral erosion, which in turn induced the disturbance of the left valley slope.

Corrective treatment. The first task of corrective treatment was to discharge the water flowing into the slide area and to catch up and drain the springs issuing in the root area. This was accomplished by ditches, wooden troughs and auxiliary pipes. Simultaneously, water was pumped from all existing wells.

After earthflow II started to extend towards the new part of the town and the railway line, the remedial measures were aimed mainly at its stabilization. In the area of deposition, several large-diameter borings were drilled and installed for permanent pumping of water. At the same time, six galleries were driven into the frontal part of the slide. As the timbering was stressed by high vertical and longitudinal pressures, the driving of galleries was very difficult. The galle-

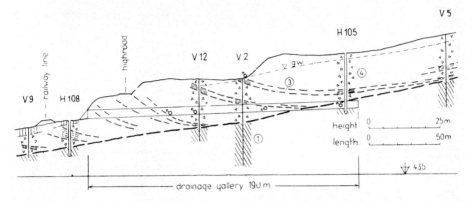

Fig. 5-15. Section of drainage gallery 12; 1 — argillaceous shales (Palaeogene); 3 — moulded clayey silts; 4 — loamy debris with andesite blocks.

ries, 100—190 m long were terminated in the Palaeogene shales, some of them branching at the end, and backfilled with andesite material. On their bottom, drainage pipes were laid. Vertical borings allowed for the reliable drainage of overlying waterlogged debris. Galleries discharging water from the toe of the slide contributed valuable data on the composition of Quaternary sediments.

The sections through the galleries (Fig. 5-15) reveal that the slope movements probably recurred several times since the Middle Pleistocene. The slid masses are composed of agglomerate and andesite debris with moulded beds of green-grey silty clay of the Gravel Formation. These Neogene sediments were displaced from the upper part of the slope onto the Palaeogene shales and the flat cones of sandy gravels spread on the Handlovka river bottom in the widened sections of the valley. Their surface was deformed into irregular waves by slope movements.

On the evidence of the remoulded greenish-grey silty clays, several flows were piled on top of one another. In gallery 12, four layers of andesite debris are separated by moulded clay beds (Fig. 5-15). As the debris is pervious and silty clays are practically impermeable, several horizons of ground water formed at the toe of the slope. In some aquifers the water was under artesian pressure in places. During corrective treatment, these horizons were drained by boring wells so as to stabilize as soon as possible the earthflow II threatening the railway line and part of the town. Definitive discharge of the ground-water horizons was achieved by drainage borings opening into drainage galleries.

The driving of galleries made possible a number of hydrogeological observations. The horizon of ground water at the Palaeogene-Quaternary boundary

Fig. 5-16. Buildings damaged by sliding masses, Handlová in Slovakia, in 1961 (photograph by Záruba.)

proved to have a very high yield. The water especially accumulates in the weathered and jointed surface layers of Palaeogene shales. In gallery 12 a strong inflow of water appeared in the fissured Palaeogene rocks, at about 72 m from the entrance. The initial yield was 1.65 l/sec. In gallery 31 an inflow of water up to 0.58 l/sec. was measured as soon as weathered Palaeogene shales were encountered. After galleries 11 and 12 were finished, the ground-water table in the neighbouring boreholes dropped to the level of the gallery bottoms. Galleries and systematic pumping discharged a large amount of water from permeable beds of sliding masses as well as from the superficial Palaeogene beds forming the substratum of the earthflow.

As the channel of the Handlovka river was constricted in several places by

52

the slid mass, several rubblework barriers were built in the threatened sections of the stream bed in order to stabilize the channel and reinforce the banks against erosion. The barriers were made up of sandstone blocks from the destroyed houses and from andesite broken in the neighbouring quarries.

In the summer months, after a partial stabilization of the earthflow, paved ditches for a permanent drainage of the entire slide area were begun. Ditches made up of concrete blocks bedded in gravels proved suitable during the first

Fig. 5-17. The root area of earthflow I near Handlová (photograph by Záruba).

two years but later they were disturbed here and there by spring torrential rains and grazing cattle (Fig. 8-3). In analogous cases the continuous maintenance of corrective measures should not be neglected.

Remedial treatment also included systematic afforestation of the slide area by suitable kinds of tree. Afforestation was not begun until 1964—1965.

5.1.6   Debris flows. The term "debris flow" designates rapid movement of slope debris, and occasionally of volcanic ash, provoked by a sudden flood. Debris flows originate in loose rocks into which water can readily seep. Mountainous debris flows are sometimes called by the name "Muren", a term used currently in the Alpine countries. As a rule, they originate above the timberline, in gorges filled with rock fragments. During torrential rains, debris and larger stones are carried in the form of a debris flow down the former stream channels. The material is unsorted, composed of large, coarsely worn boulders and fine sandy debris. The ratio of solid particles to water is usually 1 : 1. The debris flows at a great rate so that a moving train has more than once been caught and buried by it. The "Muren" cause great damage especially in the Alps where they disrupt railway lines and highroads and deteriorate valuable farm land

Fig. 5-18. The middle part of earthflow I (photograph by Bárta).

in the valleys. As early as 1875, Koch noticed that they are frequently the result of unreasonable deforestation of the mountain slopes.

Under the present climatic conditions, debris flows in Czechoslovakia are confined to the high-mountains such as the Vysoké Tatry (High Tatra), the Nízké Tatry (Low Tatra), the Malá Fatra, etc. Yet, they can be produced by careless interference on any slope covered with loose rock waste as, for instance, by the clearance or disturbance of vegetation cover, or on the slopes of deep road or railway cuttings left ungrassed for too long a time.

The decisive factor in the origin of debris flows are torrential rains of great intensity. Thus, for instance, in the High Tatra Mts. numerous debris flows were triggered by heavy rain (26 mm per 1 hour) on July 15, 1933, and disturbed overgrown debris cones in many places. On that day the ombrometric station in Starý Smokovec measured 45.8 mm of rainfall between 6 and 8 p.m.

In Fig. 5-19 there are several ombrographs of maximum diurnal rainfall values in the Tatra Mts., according to the observation of the Hydrographical Department in Bratislava. From the diagram it is evident that the maximum

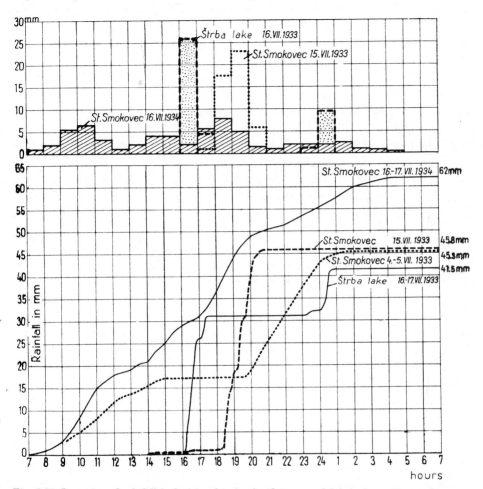

Fig. 5-19. Intensity of rainfall is decisive for the development of debris flows. Heavy downpour on July 15, 1933 triggered numerous debris flows in the High Tatra Mts.

24 hour-rainfall was measured on July 16—17, 1934, amounting to 62 mm. Because of its low intensity (5—8 mm per 1 hour), slope debris was nowhere set into motion. The great intensity of the rainfall on July 15, 1933 is clearly seen from both the summation curve and the one hour-intensity line.

Debris flows are a much-feared phenomenon in arid and semi-arid regions where the rock materials carried by intermittent floods may fill the valley with a continuous layer of waste, loam and mud. Owing to climatic conditions, the ground surface there is not protected sufficiently by vegetation from strong rainwash. The development of loam deposits on the flood plains in Central Europe may be interpreted by analogy with these circumstances. Loams were washed down and deposited after the rather sudden deterioration of climatic conditions in about 800 B.C., at the beginning of the Subatlantic period. The disturbance of the vegetation cover had been caused already before by human interference, extensive clearance and cultivation. Numerous settlements from the Bronze Age are buried by these flood loams.

This group of slope movements also includes volcanic mudflows which manifest a similar character. Volcanic explosions are usually accompanied by torrential rains which wash loose ash and minute ejecta as a mushy mass towards the foot of the volcano. Such a volcanic mudflow buried the town of Herculaneum upon the explosion of Vesuvius in A.D. 79. Debris flows also originate on the slopes of dormant volcanoes covered by mountain glaciers, when the igneous activity is rejuvenated. The heat of the eruption suddenly melts the glaciers and the flood sets slope debris and the material of terminal and lateral moraines into motion.

5.1.7   Landslides caused by the outwashing of sand. Landslides caused by the outwashing or liquefaction of sand may be included in this group of slope movements. Running sands do not represent a peculiar kind of soil, because every loose soil can become liquid under certain conditions. The liquefaction of sand may be caused by the forces developed by the water streaming in the sand. The water percolating through the sandy soil must overcome the resistance in the intergranular voids. As a result, the pressure head is diminished by $\varDelta$ h (Fig. 5-20) and the pressure difference is translated to sand grains. If the passage in the flow direction is $\varDelta$ l (cm) and the loss of piezometric head $\varDelta$ h (cm), the flow of water exerts a pressure i g/cm^2 on the grains (per volume unit of soil), where i = the hydraulic gradient in the direction of flow equal to $\varDelta$h/$\varDelta$l.

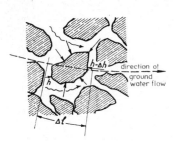

Fig. 5-20. The origin of running sand by percolating water.

From this relation it is evident that the pressure produced by water percolating in sands is proportionately greater when the difference of levels over a short distance is greater. Therefore, the tendency to liquefaction is greater in fine sands than in coarse sand and gravels, as in the latter the ground-water table has generally a small gradient. The liquefaction of sands may occur on an abrupt decline of water level, after puncturing the impermeable cover of sandy aquifer or after a sudden drawdown of the water level in a reservoir.

Natural slopes suffer disturbances of this kind only when the sand bed is suddenly soaked with water from a higher lying source.

56

For the extension of the railway station in Libeň (Prague) a gentle slope made up of Ordovician shales should have been cut off. On the slope a relic of sandy terrace was preserved, which was covered by a layer of almost impermeable clayey loam. After the excavation had been finished, small springs appeared at the level of the terrace base. After two years, the loamy cover was disturbed by the cutting for a new road, which remained unfinished the whole winter without the provision of a sufficient drainage. As a result, after a heavy rain,

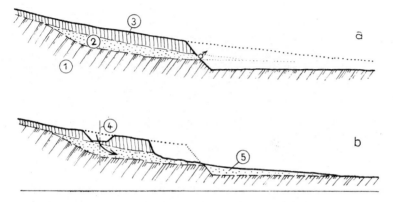

Fig. 5-21. The disturbance of slope by the outwash of sand; 1 — Ordovician shales, 2 — fine-grained sands, 3 — slope loams, 4 — excavation for a highroad, 5 — aggraded fan of fine sand. Stage *a* remains stable for 2 years, until the loam cover (3) got disturbed by excavation (4).

water seeped into the sands and washed them away, depositing them in the form of an extensive fan on the bottom of the cutting (Fig. 5-21).

In artificial cuttings, this type of slide is not frequent, because the ground-water table in permeable soils generally drops simultaneously with the progressive deepening of the cutting. The liquefaction of sand can occur, for instance, when a water-saturated sand bed is laid bare by removing low-permeable rocks. Fig. 5-22 shows diagramatically a similar slope failure from the railway construction in Moravia. An old erosion furrow cutting the slope, built up of the granitoids, was filled with sand washed down from the higher part of the slope and covered by slope loam and humus. Because of the low permeability of the cover, water accumulated in the sands and seeped through the loam downwards, issuing in the form of springs. The excavation of a drainage trench under the future embankment exposed the water-saturated sand that flowed out and produced a widespread slope movement. In such a case, the correct procedure requires the gradual deepening of the trench from the ground-water table downslope.

In water-saturated, highly porous sands the liquefaction of sand may also be due to other reasons. When exposed to a sudden impact such as vibration, etc., the grains are re-arranged, the mass becomes denser and the porosity decreases. The superfluous water is expelled, but does not escape at once, so that the re-arranged grains cannot fit close to one another. Consequently, the pore-water pressure develops, reducing the friction between grains, and the soil becomes liquid for a short interval. Some landslides of sea shores (e.g. in The Netherlands) or movements of glaciolacustrine sands on lake banks are of this type.

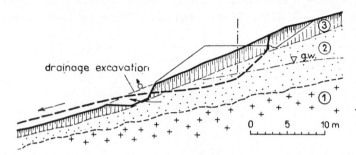

Fig. 5-22. Ground water stored in sand (2) under a layer of clayey slope loam (3) rushed out after the excavation of a trench; the water current washed out the sand and the slope was strongly disturbed; 1 — granite, 2 — fine sand (Neogene), 3 — slope loam.

Analogous slides are also found on artificial slopes, such as railroad embankments along reservoirs, upstream faces of earth dams, etc. As mentioned above, these slides are caused by the high porosity of sands and, therefore, fills constructed of them require thorough compaction.

Sandy soils of high porosity and with colloidal pore fill are no less treacherous. Shear stress provokes a disturbance of structure, as described in the foregoing example, but the superfluous water can escape from the soil only very slowly. The liquidity of such soils is not transient and they represent quicksands in the true sense of word.

5.2   Landslides in pelitic rocks

5.2.1   **Landslides along cylindrical slide surfaces.** In unconsolidated or poorly consolidated pelitic rocks such as clays, marls, claystones and clayey shales, the disturbance of slope equilibrium results in the origin of deep-reaching slumps along curved slide surfaces. In this case, the disturbance of equilibrium is caused by surpassing the shear resistance. The slide-promoting forces may be increased due to the undermining of the slope, both natural and artificial, or to its over-loading by embankment, constructions, etc.

The slide movements do not occur along predisposed surfaces, but on newly developed slide surfaces which divide the moving mass into several blocks. As these surfaces are curved, the blocks are inclined towards the slope. At the foot of the slope, the rocks are usually raised.

58

In homogeneous pelitic rocks, the shape of the slide surface may be regarded as cylindrical, as stated already in 1914 by the i nvestigation of the Swedish Geotechnical Commission. Theoretical computations and some measurements might possibly assess a somewhat different form of the slide surface, but the difference in the calculation of stability is relatively small. The course of slump-

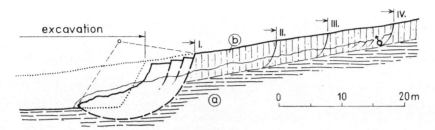

Fig. 5-23. The excavation of a foundation pit caused slumping of the slope; gradual back-breaking of the scarp (I—IV) led to the development of an earthflow on the surface of Neogene clays; a — Neogene clays, b — loess loams.

ing in cohesive rocks along rotation slide surfaces is evidently a problem of static equilibrium (chapter 7).

Landslides of cohesive soils can be found on different scales and at different degrees of development. In artificial cuttings, the slumps are frequently of a small extent, involving only a few cubic metres, whereas on high river banks or sea shores they can assume a volume of many millions of cubic metres.

The size of a slump may gradually increase by the extension of the head scarp upslope. The backward extension usually takes place along partial cylindrical surfaces, but the whole area is generally irregularly undulated and the resultant slide surface does not show a regular cylindrical shape. The depth and shape of the slide adapt to the geological structure of the slope and the local conditions. A slide provoked by an excavation for the foundation of a reservoir in north-western Bohemia may serve as an example (Fig. 5-23). As the slope of the excavation pit was too steep, the Neogene clays under the cover of loess loams slumped along a cylindrical slide surface, the outcrop of which was clearly visible on the bottom of the pit. Ground water accumulating on the surface of clays wetted the lower layers of loess loams, which slid down and had to be removed by an excavator. The movement of loess loams was stopped only when the root area was drained by several trenches and the surface water was discharged.

Slumps along cylindrical surfaces which were caused by natural factors are frequent, for instance, in the Neogene clays of the Ohře valley in the Žatec area. On steep concave banks carved in Neogene deposits, deep slumps occur side by side. The spoon-shaped head scarps are generally well developed and the surfaces of the slumped blocks are inclined into the slope. The tongues of moved material are scarcely preserved, because when they reach the river channel, the material is washed away during floods and the equilibrium state of the slope is again disturbed. Large slumps of this type have also been found in the Neogene areas of the Morava river valley in Moravia and of the Váh river valley in Slovakia.

Fig. 5-24. The toe of the Sučany slide constituted a concave, 24 m high bank of the Váh river (photograph by Záruba).

In the latter, a slide area was investigated in relation to the construction of the power plant near Súčany. The Váh river flowing along the southern foot of the Malá Fatra Mts. cut a broad valley in the Neogene sediments filling the Intra-Carpathian Turiec basin. The Neogene sediments consist of marlstones and marly silts with intercalations of crumbly sandstone and conglomerate.

West of Súčany, in a section about 400 m long, the Váh has undercut the toe of the valley slope and formed a steep concave bank up to 24 m high in the Neogene marlstones and silts. A close investigation of geological and topographical conditions has revealed that this bank is actually the front of a slide (Fig.5-24), the root area of which reaches to a distance of 900 m from the right bank of the Váh. The surface of the slide area is covered by a layer of granite debris, which forms part of an ancient alluvial cone. The area is deeply dissected, being suggestive of the recurrence of sliding processes in the geological past. The landslide extends to the left river bank; the outcrop of the slide surface, along which a conspicuous ridge of Neogene rocks had been raised several metres above the Holocene flood plain, was ascertained as being at a distance of 40—60 m from the river. The bent trunks of old willows indicated that at the time of the research the slide was still in motion. An interesting and unusual feature was that the Váh flowed on the tongue of the slide undermining its toe, while the slide surface outcropped on the other bank (Fig. 5-25). Thus the river erosion and the slide movement acted in opposite directions. In this reach, the Váh cut down antecedently into the moving mass. As the movement was relatively slow and the intensity of the river erosion was great, the two factors were almost in equilibrium.

At the site of the landslide, there was a definite knickpoint in the length-profile of the thalweg. Although the bottom was formed of soft Neogene marl-stones and silts, this knickpoint appeared as a step, such as originate in the stream channels by selective erosion in hard rocks. The step in the Váh valley,

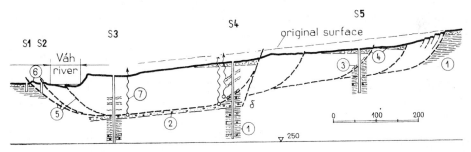

Fig. 5-25. Section of a deep landslide in the Neogene deposits near Sučany in Slovakia. The Váh river cuts into the toe of the slide; 1 — Neogene marls and sandy marlstones, 2 — Neogene sandy gravels, 3 — moulded rocks, 4 — granite debris, 5 — partial slip surface, 6 — outcrops of slide surfaces, 7 — confined ground water table in Neogene gravels.

however, was formed by soft marlstones pushed into the river bed as a result of slide movements.

The slide area was surveyed in detail and the rate of movement was determined by geodetic methods (Fig. 6-12). The horizontal displacement between 1947 and 1957 averaged 8—10 cm per year. The shape of slide surfaces and moulded zones was followed by test-pits and borings. The dip of the slide surface under the raised bulge on the left bank (34—40° into the slope) was ascertained in test pits; another outcrop of the slide surface was found in the stream bed. On the right bank, kneaded zones with slide surfaces were established at a depth of 80 m. The volume of the moving mass is estimated at 40 million m³ (Záruba and Mencl, 1958).

The landslide developed in a relatively flat terrain as a result of a number of factors, but primarily of the lateral erosion of the river and the hydrogeological conditions. The Neogene basal coarse-grained conglomerates contained an artesian water horizon with 13 atm overpressure, which forced the water into the sandy silts and thus produced the uplift of the moving mass. The movements occurred partly along the ancient tectonic surfaces which imposed the shape on the landslide.

In analysing the slope stability it has been found that the results of laboratory shear tests are not fully consistent with reality. Comparison has shown that when a large mass is in motion and the slide surfaces run deep under the surface, the results of shear strength tests performed on a small scale and on the rock samples from the surface beds cannot be relied upon. Such tests develop only one expressive slip surface, whereas at great depths and thus also at high pressures (in the case studied up to 21 kg/cm^2) broad shear zones originate, where the disturbance affects even the finest particles so that the structure of the material is also changed. This fact was already mentioned by Denisov (1951) who ascertained that at pressures surpassing 10 kg/cm^2 the internal structure of the clay mass is disturbed and the angle of shear strength diminishes.

The large Súčany landslide greatly affected the general concept of the Krpelany—Súčany—Lipovec water scheme. The diversion canal and the Váh channel were relocated so as to avoid damaging. The movement ceased as soon as the stream erosion in the toe of the slope was brought to an end. The stabilization of the slope was accelerated by a loading fill (about 60,000 m^3) constructed on the valley bottom where the raised Neogene rocks were indicative of the outcrops of slide surfaces.

In dimensions and character the landslides in the Váh valley resemble sliding phenomena described in Soviet literature from the valleys of the Volga, Moskva, Dnieper and other major rivers. The slumping is most extensive in the middle and lower reaches of the Volga valley, from the town of Gorki as far as Volgograd, and especially affects the steep western banks. The movements involve not only young superficial deposits (mainly loess and loess loams) but also the bedrock. In the steep banks, carved by lateral erosion, subhorizontally bedded clayey and sandy sediments of the Permian, Jurassic, Cretaceous and Tertiary age are exposed. The sliding phenomena occur in various forms and in different stages of development. Slumping along cylindrical surfaces occurs especially in those places where the slopes are formed of Jurassic and Cretaceous beds. The conditions favouring the origin of slide movements in the Volga valley were repeated several times in the geological past, as suggested by fossil slides buried by younger river-laid sediments. Figure 5-26 shows a cross section of a landslide of the Volga type, after Popov (1951). The cylindrical slide surfaces developed in the Jurassic clays, and the slope movements also affected the overlying Cretaceous sands and clays (Volgian and Aptian) and glacial deposits.

Popov (1951) records that the sliding of clays is promoted by their being relieved due to lateral erosion. Consequently, clays acquire the ability of absorbing water and their strength decreases. In some places, the original loading of the clays was diminished due to the deepening of the valley by 100 m which means an unloading by $15-19$ kg/m². This accounts for the susceptibility of clays to swelling.

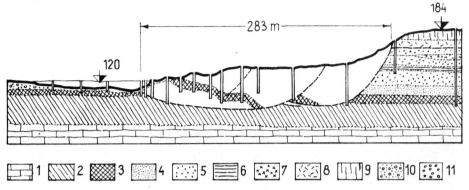

Fig. 5-26. Cross-section of landslides of the Volga type, after I.V. Popov; 1 — Carboniferous limestones, 2—3 — Jurassic clays, 4 — sands, 5 — Neocomian sands and sandstones, 6 — clays, 7 — sands (Aptian), 8 — submorainic sands, 9 — moraine, 10 — alluvium, 11 — slope debris.

The landslides in the Volga valley are up to several hundred metres long and several dozen metres deep. On the concave banks one alcove extends beside another and the remnants of the original slope intervening between slumps, form striking crests which persist for a fairly long time. Two factors contribute

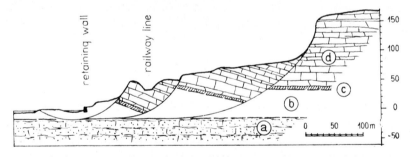

Fig. 5-27. Landslide on the seashore near Folkestone in England. a — glauconitic sandstones, b — Gault clays, c — glauconitic marls, d — sandy marlstone (Ward, 1945).

to their stability; the loading of their toes by downslipped masses and the drainage by deep marginal cracks of the root areas. The slopes of greater height are sometimes disturbed by several overlying slides. The movements of the lower parts of the slopes, caused generally by the undermining of the toes by flood waters, induce the movements of progressively higher portions. Landslides of a similar character were described in detail from the valleys of the rivers Manych and Dnieper near Kiev.

Many landslides on the sea shores may also be included in this group, as for example, the well-known landslide near Folkestone in southern England (Figs. 5-27 and 5-28). In the steep bank, upper Cretaceous rocks overlie the Gault clays. During the last two centuries a number of large landslides has interrupted the Dover—Folkestone railway line several times. The motivating force is marine abrasion of clays at sea level, which results in the unloading of the foot of the steep bank and, consequently, in the slumping along the curved slide

Fig. 5-28. Railway line near Folkestone threatened by sliding (photograph by Záruba).

surface. The stability is decreased by the hydrostatic water pressure in the fissures and joints traversing the Cretaceous rocks. Tests on samples taken in the borings have revealed that the Gault clays near the slide surface possess only a small part of the strength of the undisturbed clays. As mentioned above, this reduction of strength is due presumably to the unloading of clay and the seepage of water from the glauconitic rocks.

At every new landslide near Folkestone, clays at the toe are squeezed out and heaved into a ridge that rises as an island from the sea; during the course of time the ridge is removed by abrasion until it disappears completely. If the erosion of squeezed-out clays could be prevented, the danger of sliding would be diminished, because their weight contributes to the stability of the slope. Therefore, thick retaining walls with transverse buttresses are built along the shore to protect it from abrasion and make possible the deposition of coastal sediments.

64

At the same time, drainage galleries are driven across the slump so as to pass through all slide surfaces (Ward, 1945).

Another sea-shore slump from the Isle of Wight in southern England is shown in Fig. 5-29. In this case, the movement was provoked by wave erosion and by gradual weakening of the Oligocene fissured clay. On the sea shore, uncon- solidated grey marls were overlaid by solid limestones which in turn were covered by sandy gravels. The cylindrical slide surface, along which the mass slipped

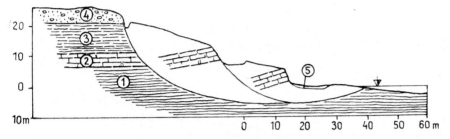

Fig. 5-29. Slumping on the coast of the Isle of Wight. Cylindrical slip surfaces developed in soft clays of Oligocene age; 1 — clays and sands of Osborn Beds, 2—3 — limestones and marls of Bembridge Series, 4 — sandy gravels, 5 — young littoral sediments (Skempton, 1946).

down had a radius of about 90 m (Skempton, 1946). On the shore, grey clays were raised and in the root area two large blocks subsided and tilted into the slope. The downslip of the two blocks renewed a temporary balance and the slope became more stable. Unless the clay ridge is protected against the surf and wave erosion, the stability will sooner or later be disturbed again. The necessary measures, however, are very expensive and can be adopted only where valuable structures are threatened.

As mentioned above, the slump mass need not move as a uniform body. When the solid homogeneous clays move as a whole, without partial slide surfaces, the physical properties within the rock mass do not show any changes. On the other hand, if the slide is divided by partial slide surfaces it disintegrates into blocks and its surface is considerably deformed. The disintegration of the incompact mass is complete and water can penetrate inside. This is the case of *fissured clays*; they are very stiff clays but traversed by a large amount of minute fissures along which they are readily breakable. On the unloading of clays in man-made cuttings, the fissures open and may be filled with gravity water which results in the weakening and slaking of the clays and in their downslip. Frost action in winter months is a contributing factor. The slides do not usually extend to the bottom of the cuttings, because the soil possesses a sufficient humidity (the ground-water table is at or near the bottom of the cutting) and, moreover, the lateral squeezing is impeded. Under these conditions, the slopes sometimes get into motion many years after the construction of the cutting.

A reasonable protective measure consists in covering the slope by humus and sod and in the construction of low retaining walls hindering the outslip of the slope. Drainage trenches of sufficient depth are needed for the discharge of water seeping through the fissures of clays. The tumbled surface of the slope must be levelled as soon as possible so as to prevent the retention of atmospheric water.

5.2.2 **Landslides of pelitic rocks along predetermined surfaces.** In pelitic rocks, slides may occur along surfaces that were predetermined by the depositional conditions. Reactivated movements along ancient slide surfaces in the areas of fossil landslides are included in this group.

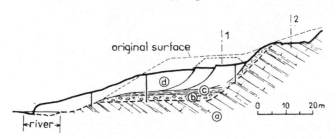

Fig. 5-30. Landslide of slope deposits along the surface of clayey deposits of the Pleistocene terrace; a — argillaceous shales and sandstones, b — sandy gravels, c — clayey alluvium, d — slipped mass; 1 — designed highroad, 2 — constructed highroad.

Landslides of this type may develop on a slope where young slope deposits rest on clayey beds. The slopes of the broad valley of the Dřevnice river (downstream of Vizovice in Moravia) are built up of Palaeogene pelitic shales with sandstone beds. Relics of gravel terraces buried by Pleistocene clayey flood sediments are locally preserved in the lower part of the slope. The slope is levelled by younger slope deposits, predominantly of clay-sandy debris, very thick in places. On the concave banks, the slope deposits are affected by deep slides whose slide planes run in the clayey beds, on the surface of terrace steps. The tongues frequently extend into the stream partly blocking the channel. During the floods, the slipped material is removed by water and thus the temporary stability of the slope is again disturbed.

Fig. 5-30 shows a section through one of these landslides which was investigated and surveyed because of the construction of a highroad. According to the original design, the highroad should have crossed the head scarp on a 3—4 m high fill, the surcharging of which would obviously result in the renewal of movement. Therefore, the highroad was located higher upslope, beyond the slide area, where the bedrock cropped out and the beds dipped into the slope. In this case, clay beds on the surface of terrace steps predetermined the position of the slide planes.

66

The reactivation of movements on ancient slide surfaces is illustrated by a landslide that occurred during the construction of the diversion canal for the Hričov—Mikšová water scheme. The canal feeding the power-plant near Mikšová was installed in an up to 20 m deep cutting. The first sign of movement appeared in September 1962, when an arcuate crack developed above the edge of the cutting. The crack was about 150 m long and at first 15—20 cm wide (Fig. 5-31). The slope above the cutting is gently inclined and passes into a wide

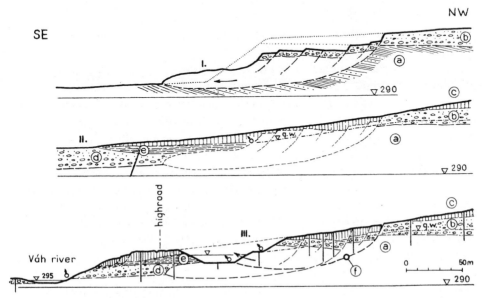

Fig. 5-31. The history of the Mikšová landslide on the bank of the Váh river. Strong valley erosion following the aggradation of the terrace (b) set the stage for landslide (I) in Palaeogene shales and conglomerates (a). Subsequent aggradation (d) was followed by the deposition of interglacial silts (e) and covering of the slope by loess loams (c). Landslide became stabilized (II). The excavation of the diversion canal caused the renewal of movement on ancient slip surfaces (III); f = drainage gallery.

terrace plain formed of Pleistocene gravels and covered by loess loams. At the site of the sliding, the bedrock is made up of Palaeogene conglomerates with intercalated pelitic shales. In the pebble material of conglomerates, calcareous sandstones are dominant but conglomerate boulders (0.5—1 m in diameter) are also found.

During the Pliocene and Pleistocene, the Váh river developed a broad valley flanked with terraces of sandy gravel and loess-loam layers. The base of the largest terrace in the section studied is at an altitude of 332—334 m above sea-level (37—39 m above the present Váh level) and the original surface of sandy gravels was 53 m above the river. In the part adjoining the valley, the terrace surface is partly denuded. In the excavation for the canal and in the borings, the Váh gravels were encountered at several levels between an altitude of 322 and 330 m. In our opinion they represent one and the same terrace that had been lowered by sliding movements. The section (Fig. 5-31) exposed in the excavation for a drainage trench also bears out this explanation.

At the foot of the slope there is a relic of a widespread gravel aggradation with its base approximately at the present river level. Calcareous silty alluvia filling the abandoned channel of the Váh are preserved on the surface of this terrace. The aggradation that yielded rich interglacial fauna, was preserved because of a thick loess-loam cover. Fig. 5-31 illustrates the progressive development of the relief of the right river bank and the origin of the ancient landslide (Záruba and Ložek, 1966b).

After the aggradation of the terrace (b), intensive river erosion deepened the valley by 46 m. The steep concave bank provided favourable conditions for the origin of slide movements, which disturbed both the terrace gravels and Palaeogene deposits. The large slide was probably not a single-phase but a recurrent phenomenon. Subsequently, the aggradation filled the valley with sandy gravels up to the 313—316 level. During the following interglacial substage, limnic sediments were deposited at the foot of the slope in the abandoned channel of Váh. The accumulation of gravels contributed to a complete stabilization of the landslide and the entire area was covered by loess loams. Subsequently, the valley was gradually deepened to the present level and the gravels of the flood plain were deposited. During this long period the slope was quiescent and only when its foot was unloaded by excavation, did the movement along ancient slide planes renew. The ground water issuing from terrace gravels and from the jointed conglomerates was an important contributing factor. The slope was stabilized by drainage trenches and borings from which the water was pumped. As the pumping is relatively expensive, a drainage gallery was driven and the overlying rocks were drained into it by several horizontal borings.

Some extensive landslides in the Bohemian areas built up of Cretaceous rocks (e.g. in the Turnov region) were of a similar character. In most cases, they were ancient Pleistocene landslides which, after long periods of rest, were re-activated under extraordinary climatic conditions (landslide near Dneboh, Fig. 1-3) or by human activity.

5.2.3 **Slope movements caused by the squeezing out of soft rocks.** The form of slope deformations caused by the squeezing-out of the underlying soft rocks depends on the local geological and topographical conditions. This group comprises block slides, deformations of slope caused by the squeezing-out of soft clays on the bottom of erosion valleys or cuttings, and some failures of embankments caused by the small bearing strength of the substratum. The squeezing-out of soft rocks is a widely distributed natural process, which because of its extremely small velocity, escapes attention.

This process has the character of the plastic deformation of rocks along a system of partial slide surfaces. The deformation is generally connected with many minute displacements within the shear zone. The differential shifts do not join to form a uniform slide surface, which gives the movement the character of plastic deformation: the sliding is slow and the mass in motion is not discretely delimited. The instability of the slope is perceptible only during a longer time-

Fig. 5-32. Block slide on the margin of the Cretaceous Plateau on the outskirts of Prague. Large blocks of sandstones are sunken into soft underlying clays and moved downslope (photograph by Záruba).

interval, after the continuous minute deformations have reached measurable values.

In the later phase of the movement, the minor partial slide surfaces may join to form a persistent surface along which, conditions permitting, an abrupt movement takes place (e.g. block slide). The squeezing-out of soft rocks can be reconstructed in the laboratory by loading an asphalt layer by a flat plate. At first, no deformation is observable, but after a certain period the plate sinks into the asphalt which behaves as dense viscous fluid and spreads outwards. The process is very slow and is produced by a load that is far smaller than the compression strength established by a current test.

(a) *Block slides* develop in places where the soft clay beds underlie jointed solid rocks forming high sheer walls. Their marginal blocks, separated by joints, sink gradually into the soft substratum squeezing it out and moving downwards. The tension produced in the marginal parts of the solid rocks tears them apart and gaping fissures arise. As a rule, the lower part of the block moves outward and the upper surface of it inclines into the slope.

The block slides are frequent in the České středohoří Mts., affecting the margins of many basalt sheets. A large block slide occurred near Bystřany in the Teplice area (Fencl and Záruba, 1956). The elevation situated NE of Bystřany is formed by a basalt sheet lying on tuffs and marlstones. At the edge of the slope a head scarp is visible, below which the sheet is broken into several blocks. These, as described above, sank into plastic marlstones, which, being squeezed out, moved valleywards along with the basalt blocks (see Fig. 10-6).

Similar deformations may be observed in the basalt quarry near Obrnice or on the slope of the Rovný hillock above Stadice. At the southern edge of the basalt sheet, below a 1,200 m long head scarp, basalt blocks are sunk into the pelitic tuffs and tilted into the slope. In Slovakia, the andesite sheets near Handlová, Banská Bystrica, etc. are disturbed by block slides of an analogous type.

The edges of the Cretaceous Plateau (e.g. the environs of Prague and in the Turnov area), with steep walls of solid sandstone resting on soft marlstones, also furnish favourable conditions for the origin of blocks slides. Fig. 5-32 shows the Cretaceous beds exposed in an abandoned quarry on the northern slope of the Motol valley in Prague. Several large sandstone blocks are sunk into soft Cenomanian clays and shifted downslope. The bedding of sandstones dips $14-16°$ into the slope and in the steps above there are relics of the Turonian sandy marlstones dragged out during the sinking of the sandstone blocks. On the floor of the quarry, bulges of stiff dark-grey Cenomanian clays squeezed-out by the heavy blocks may be seen. Cretaceous clay and sandstone boulders have also been encountered in the test pits lower in the slope, being redeposited by periglacial solifluction. The movement affected even the partly weathered Ordovician shales underlying the Cretaceous clays. In this case, the slide is a fossil phenomenon because the slope is covered by two loess-loam covers separated by the relic of fossil soil. The older loess-loam with abundant flat fragments of sandy marlstone is preserved at the foot of the slope and levels out the steps above the inclined sandstone blocks. The younger loess loam forms an almost continuous cover and is evidently younger than the slope movements described above. The clays must have been softer when the blocks sank into them than they are today and their softening may be reasonably accounted for by the thawing of the perenially frozen ground in the Pleistocene (Záruba, 1943).

Disastrous block slides occurred in the city of Algiers. Fig. 5-33 presents the geological section of the built-up elevation of St. Raphael. This is composed of densely jointed Lithothamnion limestones forming a steep wall. The marginal blocks break off and sink into Miocene marls which lie on sandstones and conglomerates superjacent on crystalline schists, especially gneisses. The down-slipping of limestone blocks is triggered by increased rainfall. The movements causing greatest damage took place in 1829, 1845, 1942 and 1943. The last disaster stimulated an inter-disciplinary research that is an example of successful

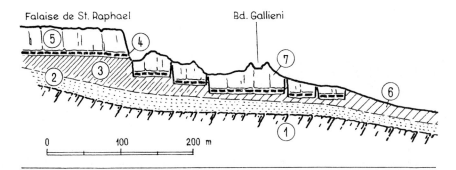

Fig. 5-33. Section of the block slide in the city of Algiers; 1 — crystalline schists, 2 — sandstones and conglomerates (Miocene), 3 — marls, 4 — glauconitic marls, 5 — Lithothamnium limestones, 6 — waterlogged slid marls, 7 — sunken limestones blocks (from Agard, 1948).

collaboration between geologists, geographers, geochemists and specialists in soil mechanics (Agard, 1948, Drouhin et al., 1948).

The results of the investigation have shown that the marls under the marginal blocks are weakened so that their strength is less than the load of the overlying limestones. The low strength of the marls is explained by the chemical activity of glauconite, present in a layer of clays at the base of the limestones. The potassium compounds loosened by weathering of the glauconite replace the calcareous salts of the percolating water and thus largely increase its pH. The alkalinized water is capable of dispersing the fine particles of marls into suspension which is then carried away. The water content in marls increases and the rock assumes the character of a viscous substance. Consequently, the edge of the limestone platform is only apparently in a state of stability, as it rests on a semi-liquid mass. The water seeping into the jointed limestones contributes to their weight, the joints widen and the cohesion of the rock decreases until the blocks break off and are set into motion.

Block slides of large size have occurred in the area flooded by the damming of the Angara river near Bratsko (Baikal region in Siberia). The blocks of Ordovician quartzites sink into Cambrian claystones. A block slide which occurred where the Ilima river empties into the Angara is illustrated in Fig. 5-34 (according to Palshin, 1963). A sheet of diabase which is more than 100 m thick lies on the Carboniferous argillaceous sediments, the original thickness of which, as ascertained by boring, was 60 m. In the stream channel their thickness is greatly reduced by erosion. They are underlain by Carboniferous sandstones of sub-horizontal dip (about 6 m per 1 km). The diabase intrusion was laid bare as early as the Neogene and by the beginning of the Middle Pleistocene the river had already cut through it and the Carboniferous claystones in the valley floor

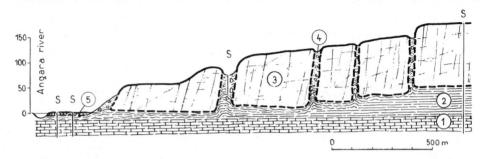

Fig. 5-34. Block slides in the valley of the Angara river in Siberia; 1 — Carboniferous sandstones, 2 — claystones, 3 — diabase, 4 — loamy-sandy infilling of gullies, 5 — sandy gravels (after Palshin, 1963).

had been exposed. At that time, too, the slope movements probably began. In the course of time the deformations extended up to a distance of 1.5 km into the slope. As seen from the section, four large blocks 250—525 m wide separated by deep fissures, were moved. The total width of the fissures is 115 m and their fill consists of sandy loam with pebbles and diabase scree.

The mean velocity of the movement, considered since the beginning of sliding, is estimated at about 0.2 mm annually. After the development of the valley terrace the long-continued deformation slowed down still further. In the Palshin's opinion the slope has reached a stage of complete stability.

Sintsov described extensive block slides from the vicinity of Odessa on the Black Sea coast already in 1898. Large marginal blocks of limestone, separated by joints roughly parallel with the shore, together with a thick loess cover gradually sink into the underlying marls and tilt landwards. When the squeezed-out marls constitute a sufficient counterbalance at the foot of the slope, an equilibrium state is established which persists until surf action washes away the rampart of marls and limestone blocks. Subsequently, the movement starts again.

An analogous type of landslides has been described by Benson (1940) from New Zealand's seashore. In the Dunedin district, sheets of basalt lava with tuffs and agglomerates lie on Eocene sands and glauconitic claystones underlain by Upper Cretaceous sandy claystones. The basalt sheet was broken into a number of blocks which slide seawards. The railway line constructed along the coast

72

that should cross this slide area has never been finished. The movements are recurrent and the tongue of downslipped material is so quickly washed away by wave and current action that the coast recedes several metres annually.

(b) *Slope movements caused by the squeezing-out of soft rocks on the valley bottom.* In some regions the squeezing-out of soft rocks on the valley bottoms is a widespread phenomenon which may occur on such a scale as to cause serious economic losses. These phenomena have been noticed in the opencasts on the iron ore in the surroundings of Northampton in Central England. Relatively deep valleys are carved in solid Jurassic limestones and pelitic shales (Lower Oolite)

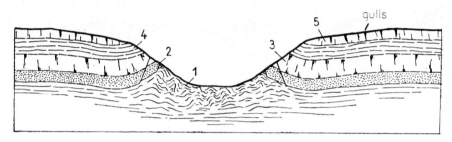

Fig. 5-35. Bulging of the Lias clays in the valley bottom near Northampton in Central England; 1 — Lias clays, 2 — sandstones of Northampton Beds, 3 — Lincolnshire limestones, 4,5 — shales and limestones of the Oolite Series (Hollingworth, 1944).

and on their bottom soft Lias clays have been laid bare. Although the complex lies nearly horizontally, the beds are largely deformed on the slopes and under the bottom. The beds of solid limestones and sandstones bearing iron ore are inclined into the sides of the valley, whereas the clays in the bottom are squeezed upwards. The marginal blocks are considerably lowered as compared with the original level preserved on the surrounding elevations. The surface limestone and sandstone beds affected by slope movements are disrupted by open fissures roughly parallel to the contour lines and sometimes contain relics of younger rocks that have fallen into them (Hollingworth et al., 1944).

Simultaneously with the sinking of marginal blocks on the slopes, the Lias clays on the valley bottom are squeezed upwards.[1] Although these deformations reach a depth of several dozen metres, in the geological sense they are a superficial phenomenon; they developed only in the uppermost beds of clay under the valley bottom, disappearing at the foot of the slope both downwards and into the slope, where the beds preserve the current, almost horizontal attitude

---

[1] The squeezing up of clayey rocks on the valley bottom is known as "bulging" and the subsidence of marginal blocks as "cambering". These terms have been introduced by Hollingworth (1944).

(Fig. 5-35). In the initial stage, the "bulging" up is manifested as a slight anticlinal bend of beds; with advancing deformation the clays are bent into minute folds and at the foot of the slope faults paralleling the valley course may even form. In the cross-section the squeezed-up beds at the slope appear as a low horst.

The stress that caused the heave of clays results from the difference in the loading of clays in the bottom of the valley and under the slopes. The deforma-

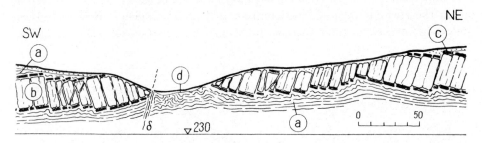

Fig. 5-36. Squeezing-out of marly shales on the valley bottom of the Lucina river near Ostrava; a — marly shales (Lower Cretaceous), b — teschenite, c — contact metamorphosed slates, d — disturbed shale beds in the valley bottom (Záruba, 1956).

tion can be interpreted in terms of the squeezing-up of plastic substance from the loaded medium into the unloaded one. These surficial deformations of the rocks and the accompanying phenomena call for great attention in engineering works. They may also be provoked by the excavation of cuttings wherever solid rocks overlie beds of soft material. Disturbances of this kind are especially troublesome in the excavations for dam foundations, as was the case at the construction of two dams near Northampton.

In Czechoslovakia, the foundation of the Žermanice Dam in the Ostrava area was threatened by bulging. The excavations and the borings for the grout curtain provided a good opportunity for a study of this phenomenon. The valley was deepened in marly shales of Lower Cretaceous age, which are penetrated by teschenite sills. The shales are soft, marly, thinly laminated and are intercalated with thin seams of calcareous sandstone. When dry, the shales disintegrate into small flat fragments, when wet, they slake. The teschenite, a basic igneous rock, is mostly coarse crystalline and very firm when fresh. It is traversed by several systems of joints, along which the rock is decomposed to a considerable depth. Upon contact with the teschenite, the superjacent and subjacent shales are contact-metamorphosed to hard hornfelsic rock showing a sheet jointing. During orogenic movements both the shales and teschenite were tectonically disturbed. The section of the Lucina river-valley (Fig. 5-36) was constructed on the basis of data ascertained in the surveyed outcrops and core borings. The section clearly shows that the teschenite body is broken into several blocks

74

by a system of faults running roughly parallel to the valley. The soft shales squeezed out by the heavy teschenite blocks move towards the stream which gradually carries them away. The inclination of the sinking blocks is clearly seen from the relics of contact-metamorphosed slates above the teschenite blocks. The main deformations probably date from the Late Pleistocene because the steps between the blocks are filled with slope debris and loess loam.

The question arises as to whether this phenomenon is of periglacial date only or whether it could develop under the present climatic conditions. Generally, the squeezing up of the substratum may occur wherever the soft rocks within a limited area become unloaded either by natural or artificial interference and where this unloading gives rise to stress. These stresses, even if they do not surpass the shear resistance of plastic beds, may result in deformations, provided that they persist for a sufficiently long time. In the case described above, the deformations might have originated during the downcutting of the valley, similarly to their initiation by the excavation of the dam foundations.

The periglacial freezing of pelitic rocks and their thawing largely facilitated the origin of deformations. Pelitic shales were enriched in water within the depth of frost action, which froze into ice laminae in the joints and bedding planes. As the ice behaves as a plastic substance and has a low unit weight, the movement might have taken place already at the stage of freezing. Moreover, the unit weight of the shales was considerably lowered within the frozen layer. According to our experience, it can be presumed that the perenially frozen ground reached at least a depth of 20—40 m. The difference between the unit weights of heavy

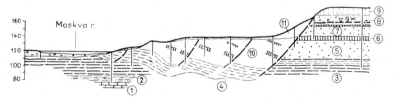

Fig. 5-37. Squeezing-out of Jurassic clays in the valley bottom of the Moskva river below the Leninske Gory in Moscow (from Churinov, 1957); 1 — Carboniferous limestones, 2 — Jurassic oolitic clays, 3 — Jurassic clays, 4 — clays disturbed by plastic deformation, 5 — Jurassic clayey sands with phosphorites, 6 — Cretaceous micaceous clays, 7 — Cretaceous sand with clay interbeds, 8 — Pleistocene sandy gravels, 9 — sandy loam, 10 — slid mass, 11 — sands with morainic boulder clay.

teschenite blocks which could absorb relatively little water and the frozen shales loosened by ice laminae was appreciable. The ratio of unit weights was about 2.8 : 2. This difference supported the squeezing out of shales, similarly as a small unit weight of salt co-acts in the bulging of salt deposits. The movement was probably still accelerated during the thaw of perenially frozen ground when the melt waters disturbed the consistence of shales, so that their complexes became softer and more plastic than they had been when frozen and than they are at present (Záruba, 1956).

The landslides on the slopes of the Leninske Gory in the Moskva river-valley are also accounted for by the squeezing out of clays (Churinov, 1957). Geological section in Fig. 5-37 demonstrates that Jurassic clays were squeezed out by the load of Lower Cretaceous rocks and heaped into a 20 m high ridge on the valley bottom. The same author mentions that the thickness of the zone affected by plastic deformation is about 20 m, as evidenced by boring results and laboratory tests. The downslipped blocks of Cretaceous rocks are buried by sandy terrace and morainic material, which points to the Late Glacial date of the movements.

The squeezing-out of soft rocks in the bottom of erosive valleys has also occurred in Rumania, where this phenomenon is termed as "valley anticlines" (Voitesti, 1934, 1938). The Rumanian geologists have studied the mechanism of the pressing up of salt deposits and described various structural deformations forced upon them by their unloading due to the young stream erosion. Plastic deformations are distinctive of the salt deposits, but also occur in the Tertiary pelitic sediments in the basins of the rivers Oltul, Tarnava Mare, Arges, etc. Anticlinal bends develop below the valley bottoms and landslides disturb the adjacent slopes although the beds are nearly horizontal farther from the valley (Ilie, 1955; Záruba, 1958b). The coincidence of the orientation of "valley anticline" axes with that of the drainage network provides evidence that these phenomena are the result of the valley erosion. At the mouth of tributaries, the branching of the anticlines is observable.

(c) *Sliding of embankments caused by the squeezing-out of the substratum.* The collapse of embankments is frequently caused by founding them on a weak substratum. High embankments are generally built wherever the communication crosses the valley filled with soft water-bearing alluvial deposits. If a fill is

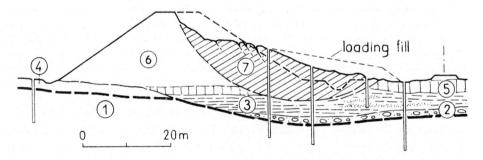

Fig. 5-38. Slide of railway embankment on a cylindrical slip surface, Podlešín in Bohemia; 1 — argillites and sandstones (Permo-Carboniferous), 2 — sandy gravels, 3 — clayey-sandy alluvium, 4 — loess loam, 5 — alluvial loam, 6 — embankment, 7 — slipped mass.

badly founded, the substratum is squeezed out sideways and the fill fails. This is accompanied by various phenomena depending on the local conditions and the character of the underlying rocks.

If the soft cohesive soils under an embankment are sufficiently thick, the slumping occurs along curved slide surfaces. The slide surface is nearly cylindrical and the equilibrium conditions are similar to those recorded in Chapter 7. The movement appears as a slow subsidence of the upper part of the fill and the

Fig. 5-39. Slide of railway embankment near Podlešín in Bohemia, heavy fill squeezed out the soft alluvial deposits (photograph by Záruba).

upheaval of the ground at the foot of the fill. The depth and dip of the slide surface may be ascertained in a trench excavated at the foot and in the head scarp, where the surface is usually exposed, and its probable form can be plotted in the section. Since the stability of the fill was equal to unity in the moment of collapse, the determination of soil properties in the substratum and in the fill may thus be checked.

The stabilization of the fill requires either decreasing the load, if the fill can be lowered at all, or increasing the resisting force by loading the toe. The size of the loading body should give a safety value greater than 1.2.

The failure of the railway embankment at Podlešín near Slaný (Záruba, 1927) may be used as an example (Fig. 5-38). The 16 m high embankment was founded partly on solid argillites and sandstones of Permo-Carboniferous age, and partly on soft clay-sandy alluvia, underlain by waterlogged sandy gravels. By means of several borings it was found that the water in the gravels was under artesian pressure. The squeezing-out of the substratum took place after increased rainfall. The material was heaved into several bulges blocking the brook channel; the impounded water threatened the buildings and roads in the valley. The railway track was secured by a loading fill built at the toe of the slope.

If the embankment is to be built on muddy or peaty soils, the squeezing-out of the substratum is applied intentionally. The embankment is built up to a greater height than required and the excess material is removed after the fill has subsided, thus achieving the necessary equilibrium.

5.3   Slides of solid rocks

So far, little attention has been paid to the sliding movements of solid rocks as their occurrence has apparently been scarce. Only detailed investigation has revealed that during the downcutting of the valleys many rock slopes were affected by processes leading to the loosening and slipping down of rocks. The deformations originated mainly during the Pleistocene; being mostly buried by a younger sedimentary cover they are frequently revealed only after the slope has been uncovered by excavations (dam site near Žermanice, Fig. 5-36, the alternative dam site near Zlákovice, Fig. 5-54, slope deformation in the Beskydy Mts., Fig. 10-14, etc.).

The large-scale rock slides on mountain slopes are numerous in the Alps, where they occurred especially after the retreat of glaciers in the Late Pleistocene. Many rock slides and rockfalls are described in detail by Heim in his book "Geologie der Schweiz" (1919—1922) and in several monographs. In the last of these (1932) Heim also presented a very complicated classification of the Alpine rock slides, distinguishing twenty types of movements on the basis of the kind of rocks, their mode of deposition, velocity of movement and a number of other factors.

The deformations of mountain slopes in the Alps have recently been studied in connection with the construction of large dams (Ampferer, 1939; Kieslinger, 1958; Clar 1963, 1965; Zischinsky, 1966; etc.). The last-named authors base their works on papers of Sander (1948) who used the term "Hangtektonik" for the slope deformations caused by gravity and pointed out the difficulty of differentiating them from the true tectonic phenomena.

For the Czechoslovak territory the following division of the slope movements in solid rocks seems reasonable:
(1) Rock slides along predetermined surfaces.
(2) Long-continued deformations of mountain slopes.
(3) Rockfalls.

5.3.1   Rock slides along predetermined surfaces, bedding, joint or fault planes generally originate when the planes of separation dip downslope and their

78

continuity is disturbed at the foot of the slope. In stratified rocks with even and smooth bedding planes, the dip of the beds is usually the maximum inclination at which the slope is permanently stable. If the beds are undercut by stream erosion or by excavation, they maintain their position only by friction. The coefficient of friction increases with the roughness and unevenness of the bedding planes. Friction is reduced by climatic factors, by the freezing and thawing of water, or by hydrostatic pressure of water in the joints if the free outflow of water is hindered. The stability of a slope may also be disturbed by the increase of its angle, as a result of tectonic uplift.

Rock slides on bedding planes or other surfaces of separation may be very disastrous in mountain areas where there are great height differences, as the acceleration of movement may proceed at a high rate, similar to that of rockfalls.

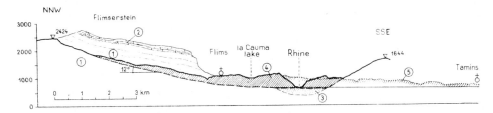

Fig. 5-40. Section of the landslide near Flims in Switzerland; 1 — Jurassic limestones, 2 — marly limestones (Lower Cretaceous), 3 — old valley deposits of the Rhine, 4 — slipped Jurassic limestones, 5 — debris flow in the Rhine valley (after Heim, 1932).

An instructive example of this type of slope failure is furnished by the landslide near Flims in the Graubünden Canton in Switzerland. With its volume of twelve cubic kilometres (after Heim, 1932) it is the largest rock slide known to have occurred in Central Europe during the Pleistocene. The stability of the mountain slope, formed chiefly of Malm marly limestones dipping $7-12°$ towards the Rhine, was disturbed probably in the Riss/Würm Interglacial, after the retreat of the valley glacier. The head scarp, especially its eastern part called Flimserstein, roughly 1,000 m high, is clearly visible and the original height and shape of the slope may be inferred from it. In the last phase, the moving mass had a great velocity and rose 150 m up the opposite valley slope above the upper edge of the settled material (Fig. 5-40).

The Rhine valley was blocked to a length of nearly 15 km and a lake formed upstream, the sedimentary and deltaic deposits of which are traceable for many kilometres. The river re-deepened its channel in the loose rocks to a depth of 400 m, so that the lake gradually dwindled away. The slopes are very steep, consisting prevalently of limestone debris, almost free of vegetation (Fig. 1-12).

The slipped rocks first covered an area of about 49 km². The height from the crown to the toe of the slide in the Rhine valley amounts to 2,000 m and the gradient is 8°. The surface of the block stream in the valley shows a mean gradient of 2—4°, which points to a high movement energy of the one-phase slide. The area is at rest at present. Flims resort was built in the upper part of the slide area and some depressions of the hummocky surface are ponded by lakes (Fig. 5-42).

The disastrous slide that took place on the slope of Mt. Rossberg in Switzerland in 1806 buried the township of Goldau. A complex of Tertiary conglomerates

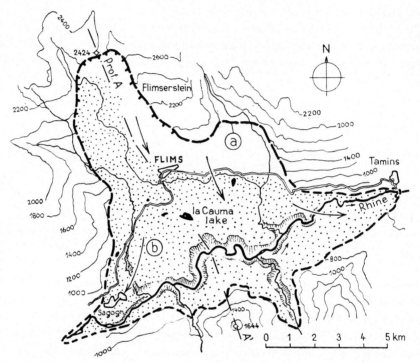

Fig. 5-41. Situation of the interglacial landslide near Flims; a — outline of the root area, b — slid Jurassic limestones (after Heim, 1932).

slid along a bed of bituminous marls dipping 19—21° downslope. The detached block was 1,700—2,000 m long, 300 m broad and 60—100 m thick. Its total volume was estimated at 35—40 million m³ (Heim, 1919).

In this instance, several people were eye-witnesses to the movement. Some saved their lives by jumping over the marginal crack, but within one or two minutes the rock stream had reached a stupendous velocity and destroyed several villages in the valley (Heim, 1932). As the slope had been stable since time immemorial, the question as to what forces had disturbed its equilibrium was lively discussed. The origin of the rock slide was explained by three main factors: (a) the orogenic forces might have caused the gradual increase of the

80

angle of slope until the coefficient of friction on the bedding plane underlying the loosened block was surpassed; (b) friction was additionally reduced as a result of the weathering of rocks on the bedding plane; (c) the hydrostatic pressure of water in the bedding joints increased after rainy years and caused the uplift of the loosened block.

Terzaghi (1950), who re-investigated the reasons for the catastrophe, arrived at the conclusion that it could most plausibly be explained by the increase

Fig. 5-42. The eastern wall of the root area of the Flims landslide, Cauma lake in the foreground (from picture postcard).

in the inclination of slope by tectonic movements, or by the decrease in the bond between the slid block and the substratum due to weathering.

The landslide in the valley of the Gross Ventre in Wyoming in 1925, was roughly of the same size. A complex of pelitic shales, sandstones and limestones of more than 50 million m³ in volume slid on the bedding plane dipping 18–21° valleywards. The masses blocked the valley and formed a temporary dam 80 m high and about 1 km long, ponding a 9 km long lake. After the spring downpours, the dam broke when the water had overflowed the crown; the flood caused great damage in the valley (Legget, 1962).

The slide of Jurassic limestones on a bedding plane overwhelmed the Vaiont

Fig. 5-43. Mass of Jurassic limestones slid into the Vaiont reservoir (from picture postcard).

reservoir in the Italian Alps. The enormous rock mass (more than 260 million m³) filled the reservoir and put out of action one of the largest arch dams of the world. The water wave overflowing the dam destroyed the town of Longarone and devastated the valley of the river Piave downstream (Fig. 5-45).

On Czechoslovak territory the slides along bedding planes are invariably small in size. One of them is the slide of Permo-Carboniferous arkoses on the argillite beds which occurred in 1872 near Mladotice in western Bohemia and gave rise to a dammed lake (Čermák, 1912).

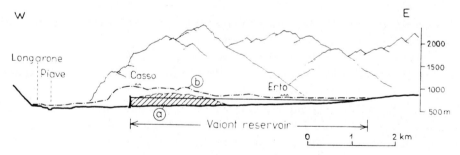

Fig. 5-44. Longitudinal profile of the Vaiont valley; a — slid mass, b — height of the water wave called forth by the rock slide (Selli and Trevisan, 1964).

82

An instructive example is furnished by the Letná slope in Prague, which was carved into a concave bank of the Vltava river in the Middle Pleistocene. Since that time it has been exposed to lateral erosion. In the slope, Ordovician rocks crop out (pelitic shales alternating with thin quartzite beds). The beds trend approximately parallel to the Vltava river and dip $30-40°$ valleywards. Weathered shales slid recurrently in several places, the last being in April 1941 after

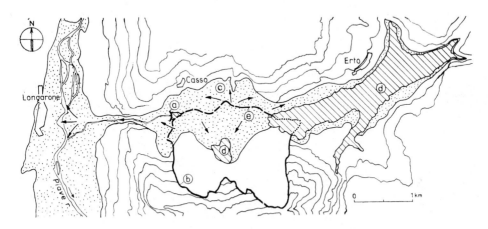

Fig. 5-45. Situation of the Vaiont landslide; a — dam, b — outline of the root area, c — area devastated by the water wave and air pressure, d — lakes, e — outline of the slide body (after Selli and Trevisan, 1964).

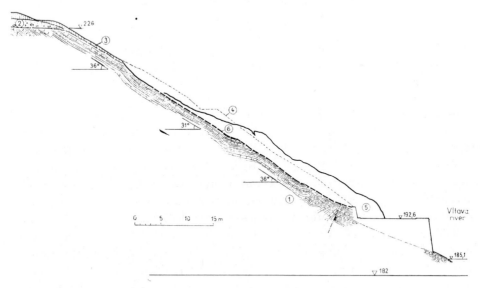

Fig. 5-46. Section of the landslide on the Letná slope in Prague (1941); 1 — argillaceous shales, 2 — sandy gravels, 3 — slope debris, 4 — original shape of the terrain, 5 — slipped slope debris and shales, 6 — slip surface.

83

heavy rainfall. A 3—4 m thick layer of shales and slope debris moved along a steeply inclined bedding plane, obstructing the traffic on the road below. The section of the Letná slope at the site of sliding is shown in Fig. 5-46. The remedial treatment required the removal of the slid material and the transfer of the foot path to a concrete bench set on piles. This relatively expensive solution was chosen because a road constructed on a fill would not be in a stable position, and a cutting would impair the stability of beds above it.

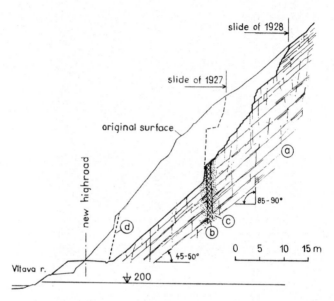

Fig. 5-47. Slide of Algonkian slates on the bedding planes, caused by road-cutting (d) in the Vltava valley south of Prague; a — Algonkian slates, b — diabase, c — contact metamorphosed slates.

Rock slides along bedding planes are frequent in the Carpathian flysch areas, where they are caused not only by the character of the rocks but also by the topographical pattern. In the Carpathians, the streams, owing to their high gradient, cut readily into the soft bedrock and the adjustment of the mountain slopes cannot keep pace with the erosion. Consequently, the slopes become very steep, often steeper than the dip of strata and if these dip valleywards, favourable conditions are created for the development of rock slides.

Many rock slides of this type are the result of such human interference as building works, the mining of raw materials, etc. The stability of sheer rocky slopes of the Vltava valley was disturbed in several places by the construction of a highroad. Figure 5-47 shows the section of one of these rock slides, where the successive phases of the movement from 1926 to 1928 are plotted. The slates dip 45—50° downslope and are densely jointed. A temporary cessation of the

84

movement took place when a diabase dyke that pierces the shales along sub-vertical joints was laid bare. The diabase dyke is not very broad but jointly with the surrounding contact-metamorphosed slates, it "reinforced" the slope for some time. The slope of the cutting was not designed in keeping with the geological structure of the area and the presumed volume of excavation was exceeded many times in some sections.

A similar rock slide (Fig. 5-48) occurred in 1959 during the reconstruction of a highroad near Týn nad Vltavou. The design prepared regardless of geological conditions proposed slope gradient of 5 : 1 in the cuttings excavated in biotite paragneisses, although the planes of schistosity dip prevalently 40° downslope. The undercutting of the slope caused a slide so that the volume of excavations was greatly increased.

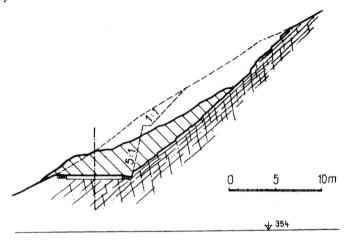

Fig. 5-48. Slide of biotitic paragneiss on bedding planes caused by a road-cutting near Týn n. Vltavou in South Bohemia (Záruba and Fencl, 1960).

5.3.2 . **Long-term deformations of mountain slopes (gravitational slides).** Besides the abrupt slides along predetermined surfaces, there exist slow long-term movements of rocks either on bedding planes or in rocks capable of plastic deformation (e.g. phyllites, mica-schists, chloritic schists). These deformations consist of component movements along planes of separation (planes of stratification, schistosity, foliation) without the development of a continuous slide surface.

The long-term loosening and sliding of rocks along moderately inclined bedding planes can originate with the gradual opening of joints and fissures as a result of climatic effects (mainly the freezing water in the joints), or with the release of residual stress in the rocks after the deepening of a valley. In the galleries driven into the rock abutments of the dam on the Morávka river (in the Beskydy Mts.), the loosening of the Godula Sandstones showing a subhorizontal dip, reached as far as 50 m from the slope surface. The sliding movements on the slope of Mt. Lukšinec in the Beskydy Mts. (Novosad 1966), appear to be a slow long-continued sliding of sandstone blocks along moderately dipping pelitic shales below (Fig. 10-14).

The long-term deformations of the mountain slopes are called "gravitational slides" in literature. They result from tectonic movements which uplifted the sedimentary beds into a fold structure and thus brought them into disequi-

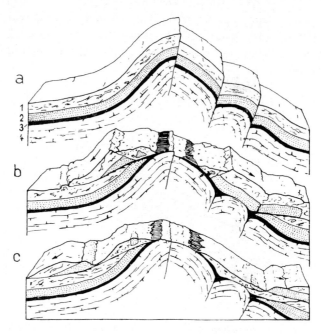

Fig. 5-49. Development of a gravitational slide (from Giannini); 1 — stratified clays, 2 — sandstones, 3 — red clays, 4 — siliceous limestones, a — upheaval of a faulted fold, b — gravitational slide of the apical part of the fold along the clay bed, c — final state after partial denudation.

librium. The uplifted complexes of beds, occasionally of large size, slide down the slope. The movements invariably occur on tectonic planes or inclined clay beds on which the coefficient of friction is lowest. Numerous gravitational slides of this kind have been described from the tectonically young mountain ranges, as for instance, from the Alps, Appennines and Carpathians. Figure 5-49 presents an example of a gravitational slide from the Appennines, where the complex of solid sandstones (Oligocene) slipped on a bed of variegated clays of the Malm age (Giannini, 1951).

Ampferer (1939, 1940) described many similar phenomena from the Alps under the term Bergzerreissung. Recently, these slow deformations have been studied by Zischinsky (1966) who recorded a series of cases from the glacial valleys of the Austrian Alps. The long-term movements are most frequent on the slopes made up of phyllites, mica-schists and other crystalline schists which allow large-size deformations through componental movements (Teil-beweglichkeit in the sense of Sander).

The section of a slope deformation from the area of Matrei-Glunzberg in the eastern Tyrol is shown in Fig. 5-50. The 1,200 m high slope of a mean gradient of 24° is formed of phyllites and calcareous mica-schists. Although in the whole area the beds dip 50—60° to the S, i.e. valleywards, they are inclined at 30—60° N (towards the slope) in the lower part of the slope, to about 1,750 m above sea level. Zischinsky explains this change by a partial rotation of beds owing to plastic deformation within a broad zone. Consistent with the deformation of the whole complex of beds was the observation of partial slide surfaces in the upper part of the slope, which indicate differential slides within the body but do not furnish evidence of the slide of the entire rock complex. The above-

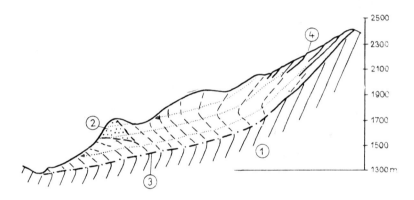

Fig. 5-50. Long-term deformation of the Matrei-Glunzerberg slope in the East Tyrol (from Zischinsky, 1966); 1 — phyllites and paragneisses in original position, 2 — carbonate sediments, 3 — probable depth of slope deformation, 4 — componental slip surfaces.

mentioned author speaks of a "continuous movement" in view of its long-term course.

The deformation of mountain slopes described by Harrison (1936) as "gravity collapse structures" from Iran, may be classified in this group. They involve Mesozoic and Tertiary rocks uplifted by orogenic movements during the Tertiary. Their origin is due to a deep erosion of soft rocks in synclinal bends and a gradual collapse of uplifted solid limestones which slipped down on gypsiferous marls (de Sitter, 1956).

These deformations of mountain slopes should be thoroughly registered, as even in Czechoslovakia they occur more frequently than is realized by most geo-logists and engineers. Many steep slopes loosened in this way, are completely concealed by younger slope deposits. The timely recognition of these phenomena is of great importance for the foundation of dams, and especially for the design of pump-storage reservoirs in high mountains.

5.3.3 **Rockfalls.** The term "rockfall" is meant to designate abrupt movement of loosened blocks or beds of solid rocks detached from rock walls or the roofs of caves. A rockfall differs from a slide in that a free fall is the main mode

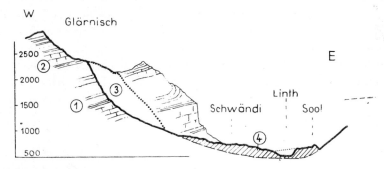

Fig. 5-51. Rockfall on the Glärnisch-Guppen mountain slope near Glarus in Switzerland (Heim, 1895); 1 — Jurassic limestones, 2 — marly limestones and sandstones (Lower Cretaceous), 3 — root area, 4 —,fallen block debris, mainly of Jurassic limestones.

of the movement and no marked slide surface develops. This group includes slope movements of widely differing dimensions, ranging from the breaking-off and falling of isolated stones, up to the fall of enormous rock complexes. The basic factors co-acting in the origin of rockfalls are as follows:

(a) Gravity.
(b) Jointing and tectonic fracturing of the rock.
(c) Weather effects, wedging effects of freezing water in joints, hydrostatic pressure of water in water-bearing fissures, other weathering processes, pressure of roots, etc.
(d) The movement is generally triggered by the undercutting of steep rocky slopes (both natural or excavated), by earthquake, and exceptionally by lightening.

From young mountain ranges—the Alps, Carpathians, Himalayas, Andes and Rocky Mountains—hundreds of rockfalls have been recorded. The largest of these seems to be the rockfall that occurred in the valley of the Bartango river in the Pamir Mts., in 1911. A rock mass of about 4,800 million m³ dammed the river valley thus creating a lake 75 km long and 262 m deep (Yakovlev et al., 1954).

One of the largest rockfalls in the area of the Glarner Alps occurred on the eastern slope of the Glärnisch-Guppen mountain group, S of the town of Glarus

(Heim, 1895). Marly limestone of the Cretaceous and Jurassic age, dipping moderately to the slope, fell into the river valley along subvertical joints, transverse to the bedding planes. The valley of the Linth was filled to a distance of about 5 km and the debris rose on the opposite bank 230 m above the present

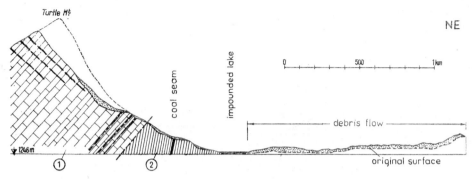

Fig. 5-52. Rockfall of Turtle Mountain in Canada which seriously damaged the town of Frank. Palaeozoic limestones slid along joint planes (McConnell and Brock, 1904); 1 — limestones, 2 — shales and sandstones.

valley level (Fig. 5-51). The rock debris with large limestone blocks covers an area exceeding 8 km² and the volume of the rock mass is estimated at 800,000 m³. From the remnants of lacustrine sediments in the Linth valley it can be inferred that the lake created by the dislodged blocks was about 70 m deep. After the river had cut its channel through the natural dam, the lake waned away. As the morainic deposits were found both under and on the rock debris, Oberholzer (1933) dates this rockfall as Late-Würmian.

Other large rockfalls from the Alps—in the valley of the Ticino river and near Elm—have been described in Chapter 1.

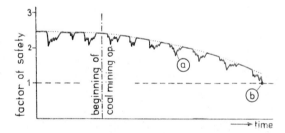

Fig. 5-53. The decrease of slope stability as a result of climatic conditions and mining work (Terzaghi, 1950); a — annual decrease of the factor of safety due to melting of snow, b — slide.

A detailed description is available of the rockfall that in 1903 destroyed part of the town of Frank below Turtle Mountain in Canada (McConnel and Brock, 1904). The mountain ridge above the town is built up of solid Palaeozoic limestones that are thrust on the relatively soft Cretaceous sandstones and shales (Fig. 5-52). Limestones dip 50° to the slope and are strongly jointed; the Cretaceous rocks are intensely folded and steeply inclined. Part of the slope broke off across the bedding. More than 30 million m³ of rock debris covered about 2.5 km² of the valley plain. The fall was almost instantaneous, lasting less than two minutes. The movement was provoked by a deformation caused by the exhaustion of a coal seam at the foot of the slope, and by the wedging effect of freezing water in the fissures. The interrelationship of these two factors is illustrated in Fig. 5-53 (Terzaghi 1950). The climatic effects themselves were not sufficient for the collapse of the slope to occur, as they repeated annually

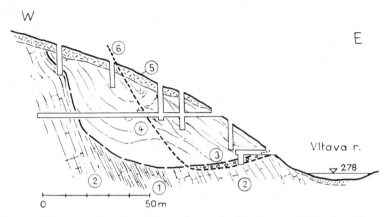

Fig. 5-54. Rockfall at the abandoned dam-site on the Vltava near Zlákovice (Bohemia): 1 — porphyroids of the Jílové Zone, 2 — epidiorites, 3 — Pleistocene terrace gravels, 4 — slipped porphyroid block, 5 — stony slope debris, 6 — inferred slope surface before the rockfall (from Zoubek, 1953).

to a more or less identical extent. But combined with the weakening of stability by mining operations, they set the stage for the failure, which took place at the moment when the degree of stability dropped below unity.

Rockfalls in the Carpathian Mountains have been instanced above by the rockfall which in 1828 affected the slope near the town of Georgheni in Rumania. The dislodged block of Dogger limestones dammed the valley, creating the lake Lacul Rosu which still exists.

From the Carpathians on Czechoslovak territory, rockfalls have been recorded in the glacial valleys in the Tatra Mountains. One of the largest is probably the fall of rocks from the slope of Mt. Slavkovský Štít into the valley of Studená Voda. A lake in the Blatná valley near Lubochňa owes its origin to the rockfall of dolomitic limestone (Záruba and Ložek, 1966a).

Rockfalls of considerable size can also be found in deep river valleys in Bohemia. Some of them are of Pleistocene age, and being partly buried by young slope sediments they are not readily discernible at the ground surface. They are usually revealed only when the slope has been examined by boring or opened by excavation. Thus, for instance, a large rockfall was recognized by Zoubek

(1953) near Zlákovice in the Vltava valley (Fig. 5-54), when the building site of the Orlík dam was investigated. Other reaches of the deep Vltava valley threatened by rockfalls were ascertained during geological survey of the dam sites between Slapy and Štěchovice.

5.4 Specific types of slope movements

This group includes those slope movements that do not occur in Central Europe under the present climatic conditions, but in other areas represent an important geological phenomenon playing a significant role in shaping the Earth's surface.

5.4.1 Solifluction.

Solifluction is a particular case of slipping and flowage of surface layers, which has been observed chiefly in the subarctic and high-mountain regions. The deep-frozen surface layers thaw to only a small depth during a short summer. The melt and atmospheric water saturates the soil, because the substratum is frozen and thus impermeable; the waterlogged surface bed moves as a dense sludge even on very moderate slopes. The solifluction is not confined only to the areas with perenially frozen ground. Under the climatic conditions of Central Europe, solifluction may develop on high-mountain slopes during spring thaw but to a far smaller degree, both in extent and depth.

The solifluction phenomena, however, were important factors in the formation of the relief during the Pleistocene. The preponderant part of scree covering the present slopes was produced by Pleistocene solifluction. The well-compacted slope debris, consisting of small and coarser fragments of hard rocks embedded in loamy sandy or clayey-loamy matrix, is generally found in several overlying layers, and extends downslope, levelling all depressions of the bedrock into a continuous slope. The debris is usually covered by loess or slope loams, on the surface of which a Holocene soil profile is developed. Being, moreover, overgrown with vegetation, the slope debris is evidently a fossil product that originated in glacial periods under a similar climate to that of the present polar regions.

In the environs of Prague, some Ordovician complexes of alternating jointed quartzites and soft pelitic shales provided an ideal setting for solifluction. Densely jointed quartzites disintegrate into small, but very slowly weathering fragments, when exposed to frost action. Readily weathering pelitic shales furnish material for lubricated fill of interfragmental interstices. The debris of these Ordovician beds is very firm, difficult to dig in excavation and resistant to climatic effects. Therefore, the slope debris with quartzite fragments is more widespread in the vicinity of Prague than would correspond to the quartzite proportion in the composition of the bedrock.

5.4.2   Sensitive clays. Of special character are landslides in clay sediments of marine origin, which after the regression of the sea occupy flat areas extending even several hundred metres above sea-level as in Scandinavia or Canada, for example (Fig. 5-55). The gradual reduction of the salt content in the pore-water of the soil results in a progressive decrease in the strength of these sediments.

Fig. 5-55 Landslide in sensitive clays (Leda clays) near Breckenridge in Canada (reproduced by permission of the Nat. Research Council of Canada).

The increase in the height differences, following the regression, causes a more intensive movement of the ground water, which, percolating through the more permeable (silt) laminae, impoverishes the surrounding clays of salt by means of osmotic processes. Atmospheric water has the same effect. Bjerrum (1955) records that in one case the NaCl content in the pore water declines from 20—30 g/litre to 1.2—2.9 g/litre. The decrease in salt concentration in pore water goes hand in hand with the decrease of the bond between the clay particles and the bound water and thus also, with the reduction of strength. It is remarkable that the drop in strength is at a maximum towards the end of the process, when the salt concentration falls below 10 g/litre. In addition to strength, the liquid limit decreases and the sensitivity of clay, i.e. the liability to the loss of strength by moulding, increases.

It is characteristic that during this process the water content of the soil remains unchanged. The loss of strength leads to the sliding movements of clays which behave as a viscous fluid. The slides extend in length and breadth and are very treacherous in that they may affect even nearly flat areas (with a slope smaller than 5 per cent). Their course is invariably very rapid. In Norway, these clays have been denoted by term *"quick clays"* (Reusch 1901), which is now used universally for highly sensitive clays.

5.4.3 Subaqueous slides. The subaqueous slides originate with the shift of unconsolidated sediments, especially clayey, silty and calcareous muds, or saturated finely sandy alluvia, along the inclined bottom. The slides, just as the deformations, may be of various dimensions ranging from the simple bending of beds to their disruption and the origin of complicated slump structures and pseudoconglomerates with fragments and galls of disturbed rocks.

The subaqueous slides develop in lakes and on seashores; favourable condi-

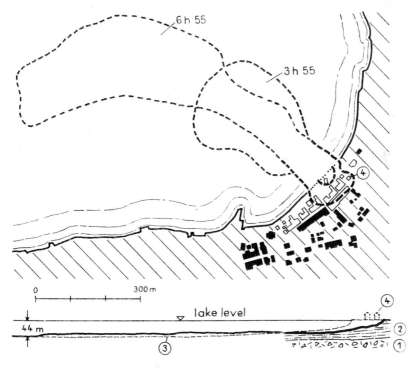

Fig. 5-56. Landslide on the shore of Zug Lake in Switzerland developed into a 1,200 m long subaqueous slump within three hours; 1 — morainic deposits, 2 — organic silts, 3 — original lake bottom, 4 — destroyed houses (Heim, 1908).

tions for their origin exist in deltaic deposits when on a fairly steep sea floor, the deposition proceeds at a relatively high rate. The movement may be stimulated by seismic or other shocks. The slides involve either the surface or subsurface beds which are set into a motion as a result of the squeezing out of the underlying soft rocks.

Cases are known in which subaqueous slides of unconsolidated material pass into turbidity currents, so that the sedimentary rocks loosened by sliding movement and mixed with water are deposited in the distant deeper parts of the depositional basin.

On the shore of the Lake Zug in Switzerland, every drawdown of the water level resulted in the sliding of banks. The slide that was triggered by the driving of piles for a new embankment wall (1887) was described in detail. Within three hours, a subaqueous slide, 1,200 m long and 200—250 m broad, developed from a slip of the bank sloping at about 4 % (Fig. 5-56). The slide originated in sandy silts with an organic admixture (Heim, 1908).

Subaqueous slides have been identified in almost all geological formations, especially in the flysch sedimentary facies (Książkiewicz 1958 a, b). Röhlich (1963) recorded the slide structures in the area of the Postspilitic Group of Algonkian age in the middle Vltava valley, and Petránek (1963) in the area formed of the Ordovician shales and quartzites.

Several instructive examples of subaqueous slides were mentioned by Hadding (1931) from the Rhaetic claystones and sandstones building up the region of Scania in Sweden. Brown (1938) described traces of numerous subaqueous slides involving Tertiary claystones and sandstones, as discovered in the Ecuador oil wells.

Subaqueous slides and turbidity currents are known to cause the disturbance of submarine cables. A large turbidity current, provoked by an earthquake near Newfoundland in 1929 progressively broke off submarine cables, which made it possible to establish its velocity at 4.4 m/sec. (Petránek, 1963).

Chapter 6

GEOLOGICAL INVESTIGATION OF LANDSLIDES

6.1 Field investigation

A reasonable project for the corrective and preventive treatment of a landslide or an area susceptible to sliding must be based on a detailed, integrated geological investigation. It is necessary to study the geological structure of the area, the petrographical and physical properties of the rocks, and the hydrogeological conditions. As the form of a slope is the end product of geological processes of the past, the morphological history of the slope must also be understood.

6.1.1 Survey of the sliding area.
By a thorough examination of the slope the extent of the sliding area is preliminarily determined, and a contour map, usually on a scale of at least 1 : 5,000 or larger, is constructed with the use of current surveying methods. A perfect topographical base for landslide mapping is provided by plans obtained by the photogrammetric technique as they show all the relevant details of the ground surface, such as fractures, scarps or changes in vegetation. This is a great help in the geological investigation of a landslide.

If a tachymetric method is used, a true illustration of the relief of the sliding area requires the measurement of a sufficiently dense network of points and a detailed sketch of the terrain.

Should only a reconnaissance survey be required, or a detailed survey of the entire area and the compiling of a contour map be impossible for lack of time, at least several cross-sections must be surveyed from the accumulated masses at the toe of the slide to above the head scarp. The cross-sections must be long enough to also cover part of the undisturbed area above and below the slide. The surface of the area should not be shown in a simplified form, but with as many topographical features as possible, such as all marked edges, swells and depressions, scarps and cracks. The surveyed sections are supplemented by the logs of boring.

6.1.2 Use of aerial photographs for landslide survey.
Air photos are the most advantageous for the investigation of landslides, because they furnish a perfect three-dimensional view of the area. On the basis of an air photo, experienced geologists can determine precisely the boundaries of a landslide, as the scarp

of a recent slide appears sharply limited against the contiguous intact area and the slope surface below the scarp is irregularly undulated, with ponded depressions here and there. As a rule, the character of vegetation on the slope affected by sliding differs from that covering the undisturbed adjacent slope. The amount of movements is easily determined from the offset of linear features, such as

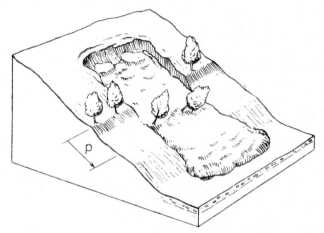

Fig. 6-1. The amount of movement (p) is determinable from the displacement of linear features.

roads, highways, railways, alleys, etc., as long as they continue to the undisturbed area (Fig. 6-1).

Aerial photographs may be of great help in preparing the programme of research work, especially the surveying plan, the lay-out of cross-sections and

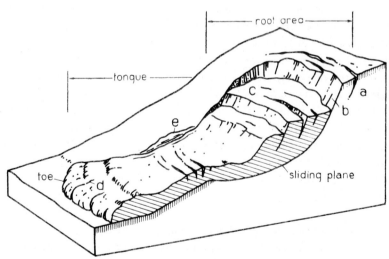

Fig. 6-2. The principal parts of a landslide and characteristic cracks (modified after Varnes); a — lunar cracks, b — head scarp, c — transverse cracks, d — radial cracks, e — lateral ridges.

96

Fig. 6-3. Slickensided lateral ridges of the Riečnice earthflow in the Orava area (Slovakia). Photograph by J. Rybář.

the reasonable location of boreholes and test-pits. If older photographs of the landslide investigated are available, the progress of the slope movement may be followed by comparing them with the new ones. Photographs on a scale of 1 : 5,000 to 1 : 10,000 proved suitable for the study of landslides.

6.1.3 **Geological mapping of sliding slopes.** The landslide and the surrounding area is mapped geologically in detail. On the map the shape of the head scarp and of the area of accumulation, all outcrops of beds, test pits, borings and wells are plotted along with the course of fissures, the shape and size of individual blocks, and the state of vegetation (e.g. leaning trees). In particular, the depth and the dip of sliding surfaces must be measured, when exposed.

An important characteristic of the sliding slope is its shape in cross-section. If the slope was sculptured by erosion and covered with waste redeposited by rainwash, the profile line forms a gentle curve at its transition into the floodplain. Even a very ancient landslide is recognizable from the convex bulged shape of the toe of the slope. On the basis of this shape, the accumulated slipped mass is readily distinguishable from an alluvial cone, for instance.

Of special importance for the recognition of the character of the movement

Fig. 6-4. Stretched roots of trees in fissures suggest active landslide (photograph by Záruba).

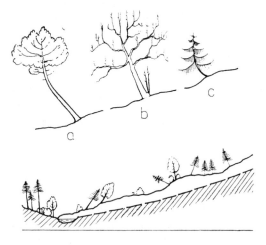

Fig. 6-5. Disturbed vegetation cover reveals recent landslides; the age of movements is inferable from the curvature of trunks (a, c) and new growths (b).

is the examination of cracks. The root area is limited by open cracks (lunar cracks) roughly perpendicular to the direction of movement (Fig. 6-2a). At the first stage, their course indicates the outline of the root area; their development at an older landslide is suggestive of its advance upslope. Discontinuous cracks, arranged en echelon, which appear lower downslope, indicate the lateral extent of the landslide even if the movement has not yet begun.

Fig. 6-6. Pines shifted and curved by sliding at the foot of Mužský Hill in 1926 (photograph by Fencl, 1963).

The head scarp is represented by the outcrop of the main slip surface along which the rock mass moved down (b). If the landslide is not so old that the initial form of the scarp would be obliterated by the disruption of the upper edge, the inclination of the sliding plane can be inferred from the shape of the scarp. On the landslide body itself, a series of transverse cracks is observable, which in the upper part are generally open and are of the tension type (c). In the lower part the cracks are closed, sometimes even deformed by pressure. The bulged part of a slide is occasionally cut by cracks arranged radially in relation to its arcuate outline (d). At both flanks of a landslide, longitudinal shear cracks develop, along which lateral ridges may be squeezed out. After the slipped mass has subsided, striation parallel with the direction of movement is observable on the ridges (Fig. 6-3).

The rock material can move downslope as large discrete blocks, as an agglomerate of small lumps or as a plastic and semifluid mass. Accordingly, the surface of the landslide can be continuous (e.g. in the case of mudflows) hummocky, stepped or terrace-shaped.

For effective corrective treatment it is necessary to determine whether the respective landslide is active, temporarily tranquil (dormant), or stabilized. Therefore, in mapping, one endeavours to distinguish landslides according to their age and developmental stage. The age is determined on the basis of geomorphological features, the relationship of the slide body to the superficial formations of the known age, and of the vegetation conditions.

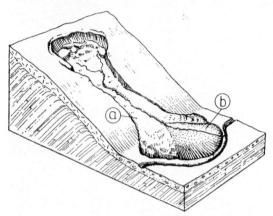

Fig. 6-7. Ancient earthflow with the tongue (a) partly buried by a younger alluvial fan (b).

The active landslides are characterized by a fresh appearance; the head scarp is steep, free of vegetation cover, cracks are open, tree roots are strung (Fig. 6-4), roads, etc. interrupted and buildings more or less destroyed. The state of tree growth is indicative of the age of recent sliding movements. Trees on unstable ground tilted downslope (Fig. 6-5), tend to return to a vertical position during the period of rest so that the trunks become conspicuously bent. From the younger, vertically growing trunk-segments, the date of the last sliding movement can be inferred.

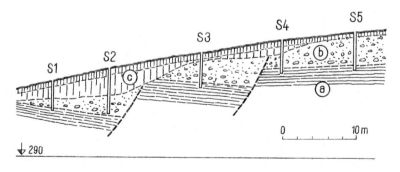

Fig. 6-8. Terrace gravels (b) lying on Upper Turonian marls (a) are affected by slope movements. Pleistocene age of movements is evidenced by intact younger loess cover (c).

100

The forms of tranquil landslides are partly obliterated, the scarp is universally overgrown and the tongue disturbed by erosion, indistinct or even buried by alluvial cones (Fig. 6-7).

The age of landslides can also be established on the basis of their relationship to the river terraces or loess sheets. Terrace aggradations, when disturbed by land slipping, occur at levels differing from their presumed position in the length profile of the valley. A terrace affected by slide movements furnishes evidence that the movements postdate its formation; if the unevennesses originated by this disturbance are levelled by loess loams, it is evident that the movement was earlier than the deposition of loess.

Illustrative examples of these interrelationships may be taken from the Turnov area (north-eastern Bohemia). Pleistocene gravels lying on Cretaceous marls were affected by slope movements in the Libuňka river valley. The steps generated were levelled out by younger loess deposits. Slope movements occurred in the younger Pleistocene, after the aggradation of the terrace and prior to the deposition of the youngest loess (Fig. 6-8).

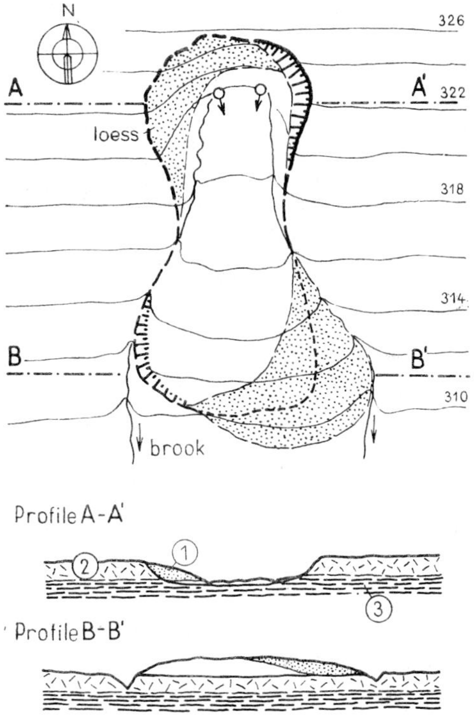

Loess generally forms drifts on the lee-sides of the head depressions and of the landslide tongues. In this way, the Pleistocene age of some landslides has been ascertained (Fig. 6-9).

Fig. 6-9. Pleistocene age of landslides is evidenced by loess covers; 1 — loess, 2 — slope debris, 3 — Neogene clay.

The development of the recent soil profile provides another tool for the determination of the age of a landslide. If in the emptied root area an undisturbed soil profile is revealed by test trenches (e.g. brownearth), the landslide can be regarded as practically at rest, because a soil profile needs a period of several hundred years for its development. On the other hand, a step-like broken or otherwise affected soil profile points to relatively recent movements. The fossil soil profiles can occasionally serve as a means for dating the slide movements, too. Thus, for instance, in the valley of Chomutov brook, in the Žatec area (western Bohemia), buried soil profiles along with terrace gravels show a step-like disturbance caused by sliding, whereas recent soil profile (degraded chernozem) developed on the youngest loess sheet is continuous, without any deformation. This observation suggests that the movements took place in the youngest Pleistocene, the slope being at rest since the deposition of the youngest loess (Fig. 6-10).

For distinguishing and delimiting areas prone to slipping, the presence of characteristic plants can be of help.

Sýkora (1961) has found that potential landslide slopes are overgrown with a particular flora, represented by horsetail (Equisetum) and horse-foot (Tussi-

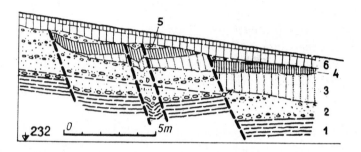

Fig. 6-10. Section through the root area of a fossil landslide exposed in a sand-pit near Žatec (West Bohemia). The undisturbed youngest loess proves the Pleistocene age of movements; 1 — Neogene clays, 2 — Pleistocene sandy gravels, 3 — older loess, 4 — fossil chernozem, 5 — drawn-out sandy gravels, 6 — younger loess.

lago). In Czechoslovakia all known habitats of Equisetum maximum are found on sliding slopes. Sýkora attributes the wide distribution of Equisetum maximum on the landslides to the dragging out of its deep-seated (at the ground-water level) jointed rhizomes, bearing reproductive bulbs, over the sliding slope as a result of soil movement. In the moist soil they regenerated readily and give rise to new plants.

In the sliding area near Dubková (eastern Moravia), horsetail was originally confined to the top part of the sliding area but the movement in 1937 entrained it downslope, so that at present it forms a dense cover over the entire slope, impairing its value as pasture land. Being strongly siliceous, horsetail is shunned by cattle, which contributes to its spreading.

According to our observations, there is a very conspicuous connection between landslide occurrences, mainly on glauconitic rocks, and the horsetail growth (Fig. 6-11). Almost all ancient earthflows in Slovakia and many landslides in the Cretaceous areas of Bohemia are covered with a dense mat of Equisetum maximum. The occurrence of these plants is not caused only by topographical but also geochemical conditions of the habitat. Chemical analyses have shown that they contain $50-60\%$ SiO_2 and $19-30\%$ K_2O in the ash (Němec et al., 1936). The SiO_2 content varies considerably attaining up to 83.5% for some specimens of Equisetum palustre. Linstow (1929) likewise records the value of $40-96\%$ SiO_2 in the ash of horsetails. Thus, horsetail growth is indicative of the presence of potassium and hydrated silicates from which SiO_2 is liberated by alkaline water. For this reason, Equisetum (mainly E. maximum) is a good indicator plant of sliding areas formed of potassium-rich, e.g. glauconite-bearing rocks.

The depth of the plane of separation as well as the age of slope movements can also be determined by palaeontological methods. The displacement of fos-

Fig. 6-11. Horsetail growth in the root area of the Handlová landslide (photograph by Záruba).

siliferous rocks is inferable from the mode of preservation of the fossils and from their relative representation or changes in their chemical composition (e.g. decalcification). Of decisive importance is, naturally, the presence of fossils which are not indigenous in the rocks concerned. Thus, for instance, Quaternary fossils occurring in Cretaceous marls indicate that the marls had been disturbed and displaced by slope movements. The depth of slipped marlstones near Březno in northern Bohemia (Fig. 10-9) was evidenced by the find of Quaternary gastropods which were displaced along the slip surface to a depth of 12 m.

In taking samples for palaeontological investigation their geological position must be thoroughly established; if the fossils occurred, for instance, in the secondary filling of a fissure, the results of investigation would be greatly distorted. The age of moved rocks can be deduced from their relations to the palaeontologically dated beds. The fossil landslide near Mikšová on the river Váh may be recorded as an example (Fig. 5-31). The slope movement could be placed in the interval preceding the last interglacial, as the silty alluvium deposited at that time covered the toe of the slide.

In block slides, the slipping of solid rocks on a soft substratum leads to the opening of fissures which are subsequently filled with younger sediments. When they are datable by palaeontological or archaeological finds, the upper age boundary of the slope movement can thus be established. A number of those fillings have been investigated, for instance, along the edges of the travertine elevation Pažice near Spišské Podhradí (Ložek and Prošek, 1957).

Drainless depressions on sliding slopes are often overgrown with fens and peats. Their age and also the age of sliding can be ascertained by pollen analysis.

After the slope has been surveyed and mapped in detail, some practical questions can already be solved. Thus, for instance, we can reconstruct the shape of the sliding surfaces and, consequently, also the depth of the slide, or estimate the number and the age of recurrent movements according to the form of the ground surface and vegetation growth.

6.1.4   **Hydrogeological research.** The plan for corrective measures for a landslide requires a good knowledge of the hydrogeological conditions of the slide itself and of its wide surroundings. The first task is to determine the depth of the groundwater table and its oscillations, and to map all streamlets flowing into the slide area, springs, seeps, wet grounds, undrained depressions, aquiferous fissures and permeable strata.

The changes of slope relief produced by sliding alter the drainage conditions of surface waters as well as the regime of the ground water. The issues are frequently obstructed and the water finds another way through the disturbed rocks. The slip surfaces are generally impervious, retaining both surface and ground waters; where they approach the ground surface, new springs and wet grounds appear. In the boring logs all data on the ground water, as e.g. the depth and fluctuation of the water table must be recorded. Special attention should be paid to the confined (artesian) water which exerts an uplift on the overlying beds.

The pore-water pressure in clayey soils affected by sliding has the same influence on the stability as the uplift of ground water. However, it cannot be determined simply by observation of the water level in borings, because by filling the borehole, the water looses the pressure in its vicinity. Therefore, it is advisable to install piezometric instruments for pore water measurement into separate holes (at a sufficient distance from geological borings), similarly as is

104

done in impermeable cores or clay base of earth dams. It is the task of a geologist and an expert in soil mechanics to decide whether the measurement of the water level in boreholes is adequate or whether the measurement of pore-water pressure is necessary.

6.1.5   **The determination of shape of sliding surface.** The outcrop of the sliding surface is invariably indicated by a steep head scarp in the upper part of the slope. The lower termination of the sliding plane can be exposed above the foot of the slope or at the valley bottom. In the latter case part of the bottom is up-heaved into a rampart in front of the slipped mass.

The orientation and the shape of the sliding surface control the depth of the landslide. If the layer in movement does not exceed 1.5 m in thickness, we speak of a surface landslide, if it is less than 5 m, the slide is described as shallow, from 5 to 20 m as deep, and if it exceeds 20 m as very deep. The depth of a slide is usually measured at right angles to the surface of the slide.

The slipping may occur on one, two or more sliding surfaces lying one above the other. In large landslides they constitute moulded and kneaded zones up to several metres thick.

For the determination of the course of the sliding surface and the depth of the slide, test pits and test trenches are generally dug because they permit a direct inspection of the individual rock strata and an easy taking of undisturbed samples for laboratory research. As a rule, test pits and trenches are excavated in slides which are already at rest.

The digging of deep test pits in loosened rocks which are in motion, is very difficult and dangerous. The trenches are advantageous in case they can be used as stabilization ribs for the drainage and stabilization of a landslide. The trench is generally dug from the lower end, in sections 8—10 m long, which immediately after geological appraisal are filled with stone rip-rap or gravel with sand-filter. A permanent outflow of water should be ensured so that the lower part of the trench does not get clogged with turbid water. When the trench remains open at a greater length, secured only by timbering, it occasionally caves-in upon the reactivation of the movement. For this reason, galleries are sometimes more convenient; they may likewise serve as a means of subsurface drainage of a slide and contribute to its stabilization.

In most cases only boreholes are available. These, however, must be made with great thoroughness if they are to yield satisfactory results. In a tranquil landslide it is very difficult to determine the position of the plane or the zone of plastic deformation by boring or hand-augered holes. In core boring these usually soft zones are disturbed by drilling fluid. It is necessary to study not only the petrographical changes of rocks but also their consistency and water content. Weakened zones along slide surfaces reveal their presence by a higher water content, more or less intense kneading and a lower unit weight of dry substance. They may be only several centimetres thick and, consequently, the taking of undisturbed samples is not very easy. If the hole is bored, for instance, by helical auger, the soft kneaded bed is established with comparative ease but it may be punctured at one turn. In this case one recommends taking at least disturbed samples of soil from the auger and, by submerging them into hot paraffin or fluidal rubber, preventing a change of their moisture and consistency. If undisturbed samples should be taken from these beds, two holes located close to each other must be bored. The first is used for a precise determination of the position of the kneaded zone, the second for taking undisturbed samples. During this operation ground-water horizons must be carefully sealed so that the rocks on the bottom of the boring are not lubricated by ground water flowing into the hole. In the exploration boreholes several slide surfaces, lying one above the other, have frequently been ascertained. For the computation of the slope stability and the proposal of remedial measures it is necessary reliably to find the deepest slip surface. The "consequent" slip surface, which is given by a bedding plane or other plane of separation, is not difficult to determine. In an "insequent" landslide, the course of the slip surface may be quite irregular and it must be assessed by borings both in longitudinal and transversal directions.

The depth of the slide surface in an active landslide can be determined more readily, because the hole deflects at the level of this surface. The deflection of bores has long served as a means for the location of a slide plane in that bars, plumbs or rods were sunk until they struck the obstacle. This procedure is not very precise because the rigidity of casing modifies the deflection of the hole and slight movements cannot be registered.

The demand for greater accuracy has led to the development of new methods. As a rule, separate holes are drilled for this purpose and are provided with adequate measuring devices. Very good results have been achieved by sinking a short lead mandril into borehole cased with plastic tube, about 1.5 cm in diameter.

The methods used for deepening the holes are varied: high-speed vibration drilling, sinking a pipe into a prerammed uncased hole and packing it with sand, borings provided with casing, or vibration driving of steel small-diameter pipes, which are pulled out after the observation tube has been sunk.

As mentioned above, the position of the slide surface is determined by sinking a short lead rod (15—30 cm long) into the pipe. To avoid the bending of the observation tube during sinking, a lead piece is sometimes suspended from it and the tube remains suspended at the mouth of the boring. A disadvantage of this device is that the measuring rod is blocked where the pipe, owing to sliding movements, bends or is sheared off, so that the direction of the slide cannot be determined.

Therefore, holes of a larger diameter (up to 10 cm) are sometimes used, in

106

which an inclinometer of a type similar to that used for measuring the curvature of borings can be inserted. The firm Slope Indicator Co. at Seattle (U.S.A.) uses aluminium tubes with four inner grooves to ensure the position of the inclinometer in relation to the tube. This device makes it possible to take measurements over the whole length of the tube and to draw a continuous profile through the deflected hole, unless it has been sheared off by the slide.

It can also be determined whether the movement occurred along several successive slide surfaces or whether it was of viscous character and did not develop any marked slide surface. The decision as to whether a simple surface or a thick kneaded zone is concerned is most important especially at deep landslides, because in the latter case the strength and other physical properties of soils may widely differ from the values established by current laboratory tests.

6.1.6   **Survey of sliding movement.** A systematic survey should be provided for the purpose of analysing the development of a landslide. A set of measuring points is laid out in the area of the landslide, linked up with the reference points located in the stable adjacent area. The displacements of the points are measured at regular intervals, or at intervals depending on factors contributing to the sliding movements, such as spring thaw, floods, earthquake, etc.

Figure 6-12 shows the location of measuring sight lines and chains on the area of the landslide near Sučany. Two former chains (designated by *a* and *b* in Fig. 6-12) were used, which had been laid out during cadastral surveying in 1947. Two new lines, *c* and *d*, were traced. The largest movement was measured at the points in

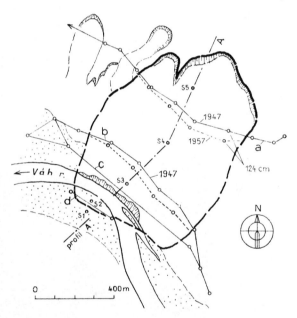

Fig. 6-12. Distribution of measuring chains (a, b) and sight-lines (c, d) on the Sučany landslide (Petrášek and Záruba, 1959).

the central section of the landslide. It amounted to 124 cm in ten years. The average rate of movement of 8—13 cm in one year corresponds to the result of surveying in the interval of 1955 to 1957 (i.e. until the stabilization of the landslide). Several systems of sets of measuring points for landslides have been presented by Brajt (1965). Occasionally, measuring points are traced not only on the surface, but also at different depths of the boreholes. The displacement of individual layers can be measured in this way. Wooden or concrete blocks, or drain tiles are inserted into the exploratory pit which is backfilled afterwards. When excavating the pit after a given period, the displacement at individual levels can be deduced from the surveyed positions of individual points (Fig. 6-13).

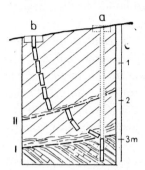

Fig. 6-13. Shift of bricks in a test pit shows the amount of movement along slip surfaces I and II; a — original position of bricks, b — their position after re-opening of the pit.

A refined method consists in installing short lengths of fibre-glass tubes into a borehole. Each tube is about 30 cm long and a thin wire or cable is fastened to its lower end and led to the surface. Here, it is passed over a pulley and stretched by a small weight. Relative displacements of individual tubes can be registered. Any displacement of the sliding mass manifests itself by a prolongation of the wires fastened to the tubes located underneath the sliding surface. The rate of sliding movement can be registered in this way and the existence of one or more sliding surfaces can be distinguished (Fig. 6-14).

6.1.7 **Measurement of residual horizontal stress.** The importance of the state of stress in the soil or rock mass for the onset of sliding movements has been

Fig. 6-14. Device for the measurement of displacements in an active landslide by lengthening of wires fastened below the slip surface (from Rybář).

108

emphasized in sect. 2.3. The possibility of the occurrence of horizontal stress exceeding the value of the pressure at rest, given by the actual overburden pressure, was referred to. Its unpropitious influence on the stability of slopes of cuttings and pits was also mentioned. Consequently, the need of investigating the value of this stress arises.

All existing methods of this investigation apply the "removal of material" technique, initiated by Sachs (In: Dow, 1965) for metals. It is based on the fact that the stress field of a strained body changes after taking away a part of the body. This induces a measurable deformation of the body. From its value and from the deformation parameters of the material, the original stress field can be computed.

As the deformation modulus of rocks differs considerably from that of soils, the methods of measurement differ with the two materials. As rocks are concerned, this method was developed in ore mines. Later on, it was used also in engineering geological investigation. The measurement of deformation of boreholes is suitable for analysing the stability of the slopes. A cylindrical measuring device ("stressmeter" or "borehole gauge") is inserted in the borehole to a given depth. The deformations of the cross-section of the borehole are transferred to the sensitive blades of the device and from them to the electrical resistance strain gauges connected with the surface. Deformations are produced by several "removal of material" techniques. For instance, the rock around the borehole is relieved by concentric overcoring by a drill machine using a diamond drill bit of larger diameter. Thus the rock around the former borehole is removed. The removal of pressure deforms the overcored cylinder of rock and from this the deformation is transferred to the stressmeter. The success of this procedure depends on the construction of the stressmeter as well as on the accuracy with which the borehole is overcored.

Among others, the method by Hast as well as the method of the Postgraduate School of Mining, Sheffield, deserve attention.

With the method by Hast (1958), the conversion of mechanical deformation into electromagnetic impulses (magnetostriction) is applied. The impulses are measured on the surface. With the method of the Postgraduate School of Mining (Roberts et al., 1964) a ring of photoelastic sensitive material is inserted into the borehole and the photoelastic changes, produced by the deformation of the cross-section of the borehole, are observed from the opening. The advantage of the latter method is that a knowledge of the deformation modulus of the rock is not necessary.

The need of overcoring the stressmeter borehole restricts the use of the method only to boreholes of limited depth. A depth of 10 m can be regarded as a success, but 20 m have also been reached. And these are the depths where the residual stress can occur. A greater depth can be reached by sinking the boreholes from shafts or galleries.

Fig. 6-15. Measurement of stress in the surface layers of a landslide (from Mencl).

The measurement of residual stress can detect "dead rocks", that is rock bodies in which the residual prestrain has been loosened, e.g. by the erosion of the adjacent valley.

In weak rocks a method to be described in the following section can be used. Mencl (1965b) presented the results of an investigation in the cutting near Bánovce. The bottom of the cutting was excavated in flysch shales. Whereas practically no pressure was registered in the material squeezed out by the landslide, the measurement in the intact section of the cutting indicated a pressure of up to 6 kp/cm^2. The conception of the factors of sliding movements, as presented in sect. 2.3, has been supported by these findings.

The deformation modulus of clayey soils is much smaller than that of rocks. Consequently, the removal of a small part of the material is necessary in order to obtain measurable deformations. This principle was applied by Mencl (1962b, 1965a) to some landslides. A hole 30—40 cm deep was bored by means of a tube equipped with a serrated edge. At the same time, the displacements of four points set around the borehole were measured. A suitable diameter of the borehole was 15 cm, while the distance of the observed points from the centre of the borehole was 33 cm (Fig. 6-15).

110

The immediate deformation modulus E_m enters into the analysis of the results. The resulting formulae read:

In the case of axial symmetry:

$$\sigma = \frac{\Delta r \cdot r \cdot E_m}{(1 + \nu)\, a^2}$$

in which Δr denotes the displacement of the observed points at a distance r from the borehole axis (σ is the compression if the displacement Δr is toward the axis), a denotes the borehole diameter and ν is Poisson's ratio.

In the case when the displacements differ in two perpendicular directions (e.g. in the direction of the slope and in the direction of the contour line): Let us denote the compressions in the two directions σ_1 and σ_2 and the displacements of the observed points in the same directions Δr_1 and Δr_2. Then

$$\Delta r_1 = \frac{\sigma_1}{2E_m} \frac{a^2}{-r}\left[5 + \nu - \frac{a^2}{r^2}(1-\nu)\right] + \frac{\sigma_2}{2E_m}\frac{a^2}{r}\left[-3 + \nu + \frac{a^2}{r^2}(1+\nu)\right]$$

$$\Delta r_2 = \frac{\sigma_1}{2E_m}\frac{a^2}{r}\left[-3 + \nu + \frac{a^2}{r^2}(1+\nu)\right] + \frac{\sigma_2}{2E_m}\frac{a^2}{r}\left[5 + \nu - \frac{a^2}{r^2}(1-\nu)\right]$$

As such a field test is very simple, it can be repeated several times and at least a qualitative picture of the state of stress field at the given point can be gained. The method is also helpful in distinguishing between the elements of the terrain of subdued topography, e.g. the root area from the area of deposition, the area under tension above the head scarp from the adjacent stable slope exhibiting compression, etc. (Mencl, 1965a).

6.1.8 **Measurement of electrical potentials in soils.** The method presented by Veder (1963) occupies a special place among the in situ tests. It is based on the conception of the existence of an electrical potential between the slope detritus and the bedrock. This potential gives rise to the migration of water toward the boundary between two layers and, as a result, to the origin of landslides. Veder presents a case in which a potential of about 40 mV was found for a current of about 50 μA.

6.2 Laboratory investigations

Owing to the great variety of landslide phenomena, discussed in chapter 5, and the miscellaneous factors diminishing the stability of slopes, statical solutions of the stability of slopes and of its improvement are often unreliable under complicated geological conditions. This pushes the importance of statical solutions rather to the background. With rock slopes doubts have even arisen as to whether statical solutions can serve as a basis of analysis at all, considering the variety of unknown parameters and of their relationships (Bjerrum and Jörstad, 1966). Nevertheless, statical solutions are often of great help and in many cases they may give a true picture of the stability. They do at least draw attention to several factors which could escape the observance of less trained investigators, e.g. to the necessity of surcharging the area above the distinct curvature of the sliding surface. If stability decreases in a pronounced manner with increasing slope height (e.g. passing from the edge to a deeper section of the cutting or analysing the stability passing downslope from the top), it is an indication that the design was wrong. This warning should not be ignored even if a statical solution yields satisfactory stability.

Under clear and simple geological conditions the numerical value of the degree of stability can be considered reliable. For this purpose, the mechanical as well as index and physical properties of rocks and soils should be investigated.

The aim of the following sections is not to analyse all the properties which use to be investigated in the laboratories. We prefer to draw attention to the need of a rather tendentious approach, based on the understanding of the geological structure of the slope and its history. This should be emphasized because laboratory work is often stereotyped and several properties are investigated without considering the geotechnical features of the problem. Often properties are tested without bearing in mind their connection and, due to the large quantity of specimens, the correlation of physical and mechanical properties is feasible for a few specimens only. The testing of the remaining specimens is thus superfluous, and this is often true of a majority of specimens.

6.3   Testing of rocks

In spite of the fact that the mechanical properties of a rock mass depend primarily on its macrostructure which is investigated in situ, the study of rock specimens is of importance.

(a) As the strength of the rock mass to a great extent results from the strength of blocks, it shoud be investigated how the latter changes at individual points of the blocks, especially at the edges and corners. Many points should be investigated to find the decrease of strength towards the rather weathered edges of the blocks. For this, the study of a correlation between the results of strength tests and those of technological tests is of help. Technological tests give only an indirect picture of the strength of rock material at the given point, but they are inexpensive and can be readily performed in large numbers. Due to a similar tendency in mining engineering, the number of such tests is greatly increasing. The widespread refraction hammer test (e.g. Schmidt's hammer test) presents an example of such a technological procedure.

(b) Strength test methods of rock specimens are not standardized and their development depends not only on the principles of science, but also on the requirements of practice. The testing apparatus should not be very expensive, the testing procedure should not be complicated and the provision and preparation of specimens should not be laborious. These requirements often result in testing methods which can be regarded rather as index tests than as mechanical tests. Therefore their results are rather of a correlative character and often serve other purposes, e.g. for the evaluation of drillability. Consequently, testing methods are preferred that can be carried out in simple laboratories. The shape of specimens is usually chosen with respect to that of core samples. To save on the number of samples and consequently the number of boreholes, the height of specimens is often reduced to 1.2 to 1.4 times the diameter. In this way another purpose is achieved, namely that a shear failure takes place. Strength tests have been discussed on an international basis, e.g. standards for these tests have been published in the Proceedings of the "Internationales Büro für Gebirgsmechanik" of the German Academy of Sciences, (published annually by Akademie-Verlag, Berlin-Ost).

The standardized diameter of drill cores is 42 mm. The compression test, the shear test[1] and the disc bending test deserve special attention (Houska, 1963).

(c) Progress of failure during the test is also of importance. Some features influencing the stability of slopes, are connected with dilatancy (i.e. the change in volume during increasing shear loading), with deformations cross-wise to the compressive loads, with the rigidity of rocks, etc. These properties can also be studied at least partially in the course of laboratory tests. From this follows the importance of graphical evidence of the progress of the test. The study of changes in other physical properties during straining, e.g. the changes in the transit time of ultrasonic waves, in the number and intensity of microvibrations, or in electrical conductivity, should be recorded. These phenomena indicate how the structure of the material has been injured in the course of mechanical straining.

The mode of failure should also be carefully recorded. If failure occurs by shear, the shape, thickness and state of the surface of the shear crack should be examined. Instead of carrying out the test until the ultimate collapse it is better to end the test earlier. This can be achieved by setting arrest inserts between the press jaws. By examining the pieces of specimen, the roughness of the shear surfaces, their unevenness and often also the elements exhibiting the ultimate resistance can be determined. Special care should be given to investigating whether the specimen failed by shear or by extension (characterized by a vertical crack along the specimen) coupled with shear.

(d) Considerable attention is often paid to the problem of the long-term strength of rock in the hope that the explanation of several landslides could

---

[1] In this test a small cylinder of rock is clamped by two jaws and sheared in the direction o f the axis.

be found in this problem. However, the results of long-term tests should be accepted with reserve. They are not universal characteristics of a given rock but they depend on the system of loading and on the shape of the specimen. Several investigators have found small values of the long-term strength as compared with the standard test results. For instance, 75 % of the standard strength has been found with granite and only 40—80 % with limestone. The tested specimens were slender in both tests. On the other hand, the decrease in the strength of rock salt with time was small if the height of the cylinders equalled the diameter (Dreyer, 1963). Polák (1965) has ascertained no decrease with time at all with several other rocks. As noticed by Mencl (1961; Mencl and Trávníček, 1964), cylindrical specimens deform laterally to a roughly barrel shape. In this way a small transversal stress originates and the tensile straining increases with time.

(e) The stress-deformation diagram of the test also introduces the possibility of analysing the deformation properties. Some care is necessary to eliminate the initial deformations connected with the contact between the specimen and the jaws. Therefore, deformation registration gauges are fixed directly to the mantle of the specimen. Several specimens of a given rock should be tested to find the differences in the deformation properties which indicate the danger of progressive failure.

(f) In rocks with distinct surfaces of discontinuity (bedding planes, cracks, faults), the material filling the joints should also be investigated. Samples of material are taken by raking and sent in sealed tubes to the laboratory, where they are tested as soils.

6.4   Cohesionless soils and rock debris

(a) Even though the determination of the most important feature of cohesionless soil, namely its density, belongs to the category of field-tests, laboratory testing should not be neglected. A dense structure of the material is manifested by an increase in volume at shear straining (dilatancy). Without this the density itself would be of no importance for the problem of shear strength. Therefore, the properties which diminish dilatancy should also be studied.

(b) Strength of grains or fragments. With a small strength of soil particles the shear strength decreases even with a dense soil mass. For instance, it decreases from the values given by the shear angle of 40° to those of only about 30°. This may be encountered with the problem of stability in gravels with partially weathered pebbles. If the parent rock was weak (shales, sandstones etc.), the fragments break easily and the strength angle decreases with increasing normal pressure. The envelope of Mohr's circles is not a straight line. Therefore, the petrographic examination of grains and of their hardness, the degree of weathering, etc. are of importance.

114

(c) The shape of grains and fragments is another factor influencing the shear strength of soil mass. As is known, this is smaller with round grains than with angular grains. Since the edges of angular grains resist the shear deformation till they break, the process of collapse of dense mass with angular grains is manifested by partial slumps. On the other hand, rock debris or sand mass with round grains collapse without any warning.

(d) An admixture of loam in cohesionless soils and rock debris should be determined and its influence on the mechanical properties examined. This may be of two kinds:

Loam affects the strength. A small quantity, of about 10—15 %, is quite beneficial, as the loam filling the voids impedes the shifting of grains or fragments. But a larger proportion decreases the strength. Occasionally, if the fragments are in contact, even more than 15 % of filling does not decrease the strength. Nevertheless, with larger deformation, e.g. with an increase of the volume of filling by frost, the contact is loosened and the strength drops rapidly. The strength of collapsed mass is also smaller than that of original material. In this sense we can speak of a certain sensitivity of this material. With access of water the loam admixture slackens and the stability deteriorates. This is why the amount of loam should be investigated when designing cuttings in terrace gravels, alluvial fans or loamy debris.

Loam affects the permeability. Ten to fifteen per cent of loam is sufficient to decrease the permeability of gravel or sand to a value lower than about 5×10^{-3} cm per sec. But at a permeability of about 1×10^{-1} cm per sec the drainage capacity of the mass decreases, and the ground water level rises if the mass is supplied with water from other more permeable layers or from a stream. This occurs with a proportion of medium and fine sand of more than about 20 %. This implies a decrease in the stability of the body. If the stability of wet mass only is taken as 100 %, it decreases in saturated soil with a permeability of about 1×10^{-1} cm per sec to about 80 %, and with a permeability of about 2.5×10^{-3} cm to about 55 %. The importance of determining the amount of fine particles is self-evident.

6.5   Cohesive soils

The problem of the shear strength of clayey soils or claystones is a delicate, and without exaggeration, a feared question in the analysis of the stability of slopes. It has also been demonstrated by experience that investigators are often blamed for its incorrect determination although the slope failure could be caused by other factors. In order to enrich our knowledge of the development of landslides in cohesive soils two ways are desirable:

To analyse the development of the stability of existing landslides, especially

115

the stability conditions preceding the outset of failure. In dangerous terrains of large importance, the pore pressure should be measured.

To compare the results of this analysis with the shear strength determined in the laboratory and to correlate them with other properties of the soil, such as with the consistency limits and mineralogical composition. It is a known fact that clayey soils differ in strength not only due to differences in water content and porosity, but also to their special mineralogical characters.

6.5.1 **Mineralogical composition.** This item is very complex and therefore, only factors related to landslides are briefly discussed:

(a) Under similar conditions cohesive soils containing clay minerals with greater activity are more hazardous. Claystones and clayey shales with their layers of montmorillonitic clay are especially troublesome. The swelling of clay layers is followed by the development of tensile cracks in rather stiff beds of shales. The cracks are very close to one another and the rock changes into a mass with the character of a fissured clay. Mencl (1962a) determined the shear strength of such a rock mass (flysch of Palaeogene age) as characterized by an angle of $\varphi = 14$ degrees (tan $\varphi = 0.25$). The landslide did not occur until ten months after the excavation. Probably the smallest values of strength have been evidenced by Underwood (1964) at the Harlan project (a tributary of the Missouri river). Cretaceous marlstone with interbeds containing 80 % montmorillonite, exhibited a strength in field tests

$$\tau = 0.15 + 0.13 \cdot \sigma \ (kg/cm^2)$$

(b) The influence of the sorbed cations on the behaviour of soils in a slope is controlled by three factors:

The soil may contain either only adsorbed water or also free water. In the former case the accepted phenomenon that the cations with a small radius and a high valency produce high shear strength holds true; it is associated with the distance between particles. Kazda (1961) found that with a water content of 10 per cent (as is encountered with claystones) the strength of the Ca-form of clays was several times greater than that of the Na-form. On the contrary, if free water is also present, the Ca-form is capable of attracting less water than the Na-form, which is evident by the tendency to slake. Already in 1947 Bernatzik pointed out that a clay weakened at contact with a cement grouting mixture.

Another factor of importance associated with landslides is the remoulding of soil mass. The behaviour of remoulded illitic clays differs from that of montmorillonitic ones. The change into a K-form increases the strength of illitic clays in the undisturbed as well as in the remoulded state. On the other hand, K-ions cause a closer arrangement of elementary layers in montmorillonitic clays. This results in the squeezing out of some quantity of free water and thus,

116

in decreased strength after remoulding. This is of practical importance near the surface of slopes, as K-ions loosened by weathering increase the strength of illitic clays but can have an unpropitious effect on montmorillonitic clays in unstable areas.

The nature of cations can also affect the rate of consolidation. A higher valency and smaller hydrated ion diameter increase not only the strength but also the permeability. On the other hand, the permeability of Na-forms is small. The anions also increase the permeability, and thus the effectiveness of the drainage trenches on the slopes in fissured clays. Slag enriches the soil with anions and the permeability increases.

(c) The third problem concerns the weathering of clayey soils, the decomposition of which affects iron compounds; on oxidizing, the crystal lattice of clay elements disintegrates and cations, especially K-ions, are loosened. This disintegration appeared in the upper section (in the earthflow) of the landslide at Handlová.

(d) K-ions can also be supplied by the overlying beds. The susceptibility of glauconite-bearing sandstones of the Bohemian Cretaceous formation to sliding may be explained in this way. The seepage water intervenes, because K-ions are loosened from glauconite by an ion-exchange process. K-ions substitute Ca-ions and the concentration of H-ions changes. Alkalinized water induces the dispersion of subgrade clays and transforms them into a suspension, which is transported by water, thus impairing the mechanical properties of individual clay strata.

6.5.2 **The Atterberg limits prove to be good index characteristics of the nature of clayey soils.** Therefore, their determination and their significance should be considered. When a landslide occurs in surface layers, the change in the Atterberg limits should be followed along the depth of the boreholes. They should be correlated with the mechanical properties. When dealing with this question we must not forget that the Atterberg limits are determined on specimens of remoulded soil. Therefore, cations of high valency contribute to a reduction of the liquid limit of montmorillonitic clays, as water is also loosened from their lattice. On the other hand, clays exhibiting no sorption capacity of the crystal lattice, as for instance, kaolinitic or illitic clays, present the opposite results: Na-illite yields a low value of the liquid limit and K^+, Mg^{2+}, Ca^{2+}, Fe^{3+} forms follow Kazda, 1961b).

The same sequence — K^+, Mg^{2+}, Ca^{2+}, Fe^{3+} — is encountered when examining the plastic limit.

There is no doubt that the values of the Atterberg limits are associated with the mineralogical composition of the clay fraction. The latter is studied by means of chemical, X-ray and differential thermal analyses. Since this fraction can be present in a larger or smaller proportion, the Atterberg limits are also affected by the amount of clay particles. Therefore, the values of the Atterberg limits cannot be simply correlated with the mineralogical composition of the given clayey soil. A proportion of clay fraction should be considered, too. This leads to the evaluation of the so-called activity of clays, i.e. the ratio of the plasticity index to the percentage of particles smaller than 0.002 mm by weight. The activity is universally noted in reports, but care is necessary when determining the percentage of particles smaller than 0.002 mm. It is not easy and often the results are wrong, mostly due to coagulation. Since the activity is compared with the values presented by Skempton (1948, 1953), which are based on a size analysis using British standard methods, these methods should be employed. This especially concerns the treatment of the soil and the nature of the dispersing agents used to prevent coagulation.

6.5.3 **Strength of cohesive soils.** The third important problem is the determination of strength. Three modalities may occur:

(a) The strength is studied in soils not yet injured by landslide movements and by climatic factors such as repeated drying and saturation.

(b) The strength is to be found as it developed after the soils have been affected by climatic factors, but not by landslide movements.

(c) The strength of a soil mass disturbed by sliding movement.

Undisturbed samples, unaffected by transport, are necessary in the first case. As shown in Chapter 2, the best method of testing is by modelling the process of loading after that which occurs in the field. Therefore, at the beginning of the test the load should correspond to the stress conditions in the field prior to construction (Fig. 6-16a). If horizontal residual stresses have not been measured in field conditions, it is advisable to begin with the hydrostatic pressure

$$\sigma_x = \sigma_z = \gamma z \text{ (point } a \text{ in Fig. 6-16c).}$$

If pore water pressure has been measured, it is necessary to subject the specimen to its influence. Therefore triaxial compression tests, which make the measurement and control of the pore water pressure possible, are best suited. If the piezometric water level is at the elevation z_0 above the investigated point n, the starting point a in the Mohr diagram is translated by $\gamma_w z_0$ to the left (to a', Fig. 6-16c).

Afterwards, changes in stress conditions as well as pore water pressure are imitated, as they are assumed to develop during the excavation of the cutting, considering the state after consolidation. The values σ_1' and σ_2' are decreased gradually, as they decrease in the course of excavation. In this way, the state of stress, given by point a (or a') at the beginning, changes into a state represented by Mohr's circle K_b'. Step by step the final state of stress is achieved (circle K_c'), as it occurs after the full excavation. However, the process of testing should be continued up to the state represented by the circle K_f', when the soil resistance is overwhelmed. As a rule, the test is repeated and as identical values σ' cannot then be achieved, several Mohr's circles K_f' are obtained. From them the envelope M can be drawn, which represents the strength valid for point n and for its neighbourhood. In a similar way, the envelope for the point $n + 1$ and for several other points of the potential slip surface is determined. The sections of envelopes are then connected by the line of strength M.

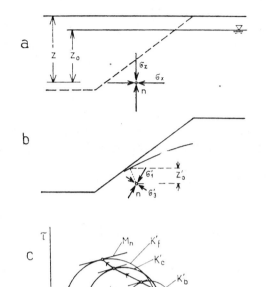

As emphasized in Chapter 2, care is necessary when dealing with points at which the slip surface comes near to the surface of the soil mass and, consequently, at which the normal stress is small. This is often further reduced by the seepage forces of ground water percolating towards the surface. In the domain of small σ' the line M curves downwards, the strength decreases substantially, since the soil has swollen and its water content has increased.

In Neogene clays of the Carpathian Foredeep this turn of the line M corresponds to $\sigma' = 0.4 \div 0.5$ kp/cm². With larger σ' the line is nearly straight and its inclination is represented by the angle of shear strength $\sigma' = 18$ to 19 degrees. Its imaginary prolongation yields

Fig. 6-16. Before excavation, the state of stress in point n is represented by a circle reduced to point a (in total stresses) or a' (in effective stresses). During excavation, the stress a' passes through state given by circle K_b' to the final state K_c'. Additional impairment of the state of stress would result in state K_f' of a complete failure. Thus a point of the line of strength M_n is given.

$c' = 0.7$ kp/cm² with $w = 25\,\%$ (about the plastic limit),

$c' = 0.5$ kp/cm² with $w = 28\,\%$, on the axis of ordinates.

On the basis of analyses of existing landslides several authors (Gould, 1960) recently recommended not applying the peak value strength parameters for the design of slopes (as a rule associated with a factor of safety of 1.5). On the contrary, they advocate the application of the strength as it appears after the slip surface has developed (the so-called residual strength), even if the stability of an intact slope is analysed, i.e. if slip surfaces are not supposed to develop. As a reason for this approach, different existing structural features are pointed out which, as a rule, reduce the resistance of the soil mass but remain unnoticed during exploration. A factor of safety a bit larger than one is sufficient in this case.

For this purpose shear tests are necessary, which allow to measure the soil resistance even after the slip surface has developed, i.e. after the peak value of the strength has been surpassed and the specimen has failed by shear. The torsional shear test belongs to this category. Due to difficulties associated with the preparation of samples with this method, direct shear tests in shear box apparatus are preferred. Yet, the two halves of the box are displaced too much one against the other prior to the attainment of the residual strength. Therefore, the test is prolonged up to a large displacement, after which both the box halves are put back and the tests repeated from zero position but with an already developed slip surface.

The residual shear strength of the Neogene clay as referred to in the preceding paragraph is given by the parameters $\varphi'_R = 16$ degrees and c' very small (about 0.05 kp/cm²).

A theoretically simpler question appears to be that of the stability of surface soil layers subjected to the influence of climatic factors. Slip surfaces parallel to the surface are considered. The technique of testing, however, is impaired by the existence of numerous cracks which give the soil the character of fissured clay. Since the surface layer is often stiffened by the addition of K-ions (section 6.5.1), sliding movements generally occur along a slip surface located several metres underneath the surface. Soils in old landslide areas with healed slip surfaces present the picture of fissured clays. The hydrostatic pressure of water filling the fissures may contribute to the reduction of stability.

As fissures decrease the strength of soils, they should be present in samples subjected to shear tests. However, the shear strength is usually a bit higher than with materials having a developed shear surface, since the joints are uneven and of irregular pattern.

As the unpropitious effect of the joints on the strength is the more significant the lower the normal stress, the strength curve in Mohr's diagram is not a straight line.

Thus, the shear strength of surface layers of Neogene clays can be characterized by parameters:

with $\sigma' = 0.5$ kp/cm² : $c' = 0.2$ kp/cm², $\varphi = 18$ degrees

$\sigma' = 0.25$ kp/cm² : $c' = 0$ kp/cm², $\varphi = 20$ degrees

Gould (1960) assumed for montmorillonitic clays

$c' = 0$ $\varphi' = 12 - 14$ degrees.

Recent landslides belong to a third category. The slip surface is usually

120

polished and practically no cohesion exists. During the test, it is necessary to prolong the displacements of the halves of the box, in order to obtain the true low values of resistance valid for the polished surfaces.

Generally a good picture of the stability can be obtained if the angle of true friction is taken as a basis. This term needs an explanation, for students of engineering geology are not acquainted with the testing of soils. It can be easily explained by considering that the soil becomes stiffer through the process of consolidation. By the pressing out of pore water from the clay soil, the particles are packed closer together and the molecular bonds increase. Consequently, cohesive forces increase as σ' increases. Therefore, if the shear strength of clayey soil is represented by a straight line with the inclination of tan φ' in Mohr's diagram, the increase of τ' is partly due to the increase in cohesion and partly to the true friction.

Thus, for the Neogene clay, the total angle of shear strength is about 22 degrees. In this the true friction is represented by an angle of about 15 degrees. The determination of this component requires some knowledge of laboratory techniques. Therefore, workers trained in soil mechanics laboratories should be put in charge of this task.

6.5.4 **Determination of the immediate modulus of deformation.** The technique of the measurement of residual stress in soil mass was discussed in sect. 6.1.7. Its importance for the stability of slopes was emphasized in sect. 2.3. The elaboration of the results requires a knowledge of the immediate modulus of deformation, i.e. of deformation in the absence of consolidation. This can be measured either by rapid loading tests in the field or by rapid laboratory compression tests. Cylindrical soil specimens are subjected to compression equal to about one-third of the compression strength. Cylinders of larger diameter are preferred since local irregularities are effective. Ten centimetres is a suitable diameter with a height of about 12—14 cm. The buckling of high cylinders considerably reduces the measured modulus.

The modulus of deformation is computed from the increment in stress (in the stress domain about one-third the strength) and from that in strain. For Neogene clay Mencl (1966a) obtained a value of about 500 kp/cm², which is about three times the modulus under full consolidation.

6.5.5 **Rate of consolidation under compression.** Several stability problems, e.g. those where the weight of the fill is expected to increase the strength of the underlying soil by consolidation, require the investigation of the rate of consolidation. Two cases are most frequently encountered:

A counter dam is constructed (Fig. 6-17) to stabilize the slope and the question to be decided is whether or not the consolidation of the underlying soil will be achieved in due course.

When analysing this problem, another aspect should be considered, namely that the soil will be not only compressed but also sheared by the horizontal forces. Consequently, consolidation under the action of these forces is also necessary (sect. 2.2b).

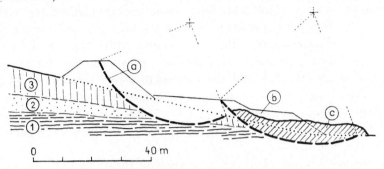

Fig. 6-17. Landslide (a) involving the substratum was caused by the load of road embankment. The slope was stabilized by a counter dam (b) which, however, provoked further sliding (c). 1 — Neogene clay, 2 — glaciofluvial sand, 3 — loess loam.

The time rate of consolidation is investigated by oedometer tests on undisturbed samples in the laboratory. Readings of the compression at short intervals are necessary: in the first 5 minutes, each half minute, and later on each 5 minutes, etc. It is advisable to begin the test with the pressure corresponding to the weight of the overburden in nature and to increase it step by step up to the required pressure. The theory of consolidation allows us to calculate the degree of consolidation in the field from the results of laboratory tests.

Chapter 7

INTERPRETATION OF EXPLORATION AND STABILITY ANALYSIS

7.1 Preliminary analysis during exploratory work

Soon after the beginning of exploratory work the stability of the slope or of the landslide should be analysed. This rule is often neglected in current practice, and the stability analysis is postponed until the exploration has been completed. This approach can be tolerated only when dealing with problems of minor importance. Lack of information on the significance of the factors contributing to the statical behaviour of the slope is a serious drawback. Without them we are not able to judge whether the results of exploration are correct or not, and we cannot control the further stages of exploration. On the other hand, if the preliminary statical solution has been carried out and if its results are confusing, we can try to detect the reasons and change the extent or the methods of exploration. A proper and timely assessment of results is thus a guide to more precise field and laboratory explorations.

The investigation of the landslide near Klačany on the river Váh (Záruba and Mencl, 1958) can be cited as an example. The preliminary field exploration resulted in a simple working hypothesis of the exclusive importance of river erosion and the uplift of ground-water for the development of this landslide. Exploratory boreholes gave a good picture of the ground-water level in more permeable seams of sand in the clay mass and yielded samples for laboratory investigation of shear strength. The statical analysis, however, showed a satisfactory stability of the slope. The assumption that the slope had been higher in the past could not be accepted since the elevation was fixed by the presence of alluvial fan deposits on the surface of the landslide mass. Therefore, detailed investigation of the site was carried out, which resulted in the recognition of tectonically predisposed surfaces as a third important factor of failure.

The interpretation of investigation resnlts should, as far as possible, always lead to a stability analysis of the slope. Two categories of problems are to be distinguished:

(a) The design of cuttings and fills in areas susceptible to sliding, but as yet still stable.

(b) The stabilization of existing landslides.

123

7.2   The design of cuttings

There is no doubt that this problem is of great economic importance and that the final solution should be selected by checking more alternatives. The choice is simplified by the tendency towards mechanizing excavation works. It appears that—where technically feasible—the solution involving earthwork of larger volumes is more economical than that proposing the use of walls or tunnels. The excavation of drainage trenches and galleries can also be superseded by drilling horizontal drainage boreholes. The factor of time should be considered, too. The progress of excavation works can be hindered by inadequate progress in other works (e.g. bolting, excavation of drainage trenches etc.), since premature excavation could invalidate the stability of slopes. Therefore, when combining several operations, it is necessary to work out a detailed schedule and guarantee its realization. The designers should not only seek for a most economical combination of components of design with regard to standard costs, but also consider the real conditions of the site, affected by unfavourable climatic factors, etc. A delay due to complicated and elaborate constructional operations may often result in greater economic losses than the apparently attained savings. Therefore, generally simple solutions are chosen today and the designer is required to correctly assess the shape of slopes. When designing the slopes, the general stability as well as the danger of progressive failure must be considered. Small, often unnoticed disturbed areas can grow into large landslides, especially if water is present. The constructional works necessitated by the interference of atmospheric agents will be discussed in Chapter 8. The subject of the present chapter is the stability of slopes in general.

The methods of design of slopes are known. The problem is solved by applying the principles of limit plastic equilibrium design, i.e. by the examination of the factor of safety defined by the ratio of resisting forces (or of their products, e.g. moments) to the driving forces. This method deals with imaginary state of failure, the existence of which is excluded if the factor of safety is satisfactory, e.g. 1.5 for cohesive soils. As discussed in sect. 2.2a, first cracks occur with a smaller factor of about 1.3. Their formation enables climatic agents to attack the material. It is to be expected that the analysis of processes connected with progressive deterioration of the slope will yield a more precise method of the design of slopes. In the mean time the limit plastic equilibrium analysis is to be used and an adequate factor of safety is to be required. Partial questions arise, as to the shape of the slip surface (sect. 7.2.1), the magnitude of the active forces (7.2.2), the strength of the material (7.2.3), the required magnitude of the factor of safety (7.2.4) and the proper stability analysis (7.2.5).

7.2.1   **The shape of the slip surface.** This question has been partially discussed in sect. 2.2c. In practice the following three solutions may be considered:

(a) The slip surface is predisposed according to geological conditions of the site. Bedding planes, faults or slip surfaces of old landslides often yield the smallest factor of safety. A typical example of a landslide along bedding planes was the Vaiont slide (Fig. 7-10), that of the movement along faults the slide near Sučany (Fig. 5-25) and that along old slip surfaces, the failure of a cutting of the canal near Mikšová (Fig. 5-31). In the given cases the statical solutions were on the one hand facilitated by the fact that the slip surface was known and on the other hand, complicated owing to its varying curvature.

(b) Straight slip planes are assumed to exist within sandy soils and rock debris, as the slope slides in layers of small thickness until an equilibrium is reached.

(c) For the purpose of stability analysis, slip surfaces in homogeneous cohesive soils are assumed to have the shape of circular cylinders. This is rather a simplification of reality, as e.g. the surfaces with cross-sections in the shape of logarithmic spirals give a somewhat smaller stability (sect. 2.2c). But the majority of the elaborated methods of solution assume a circular shape of the slip surface and several of them were set up in diagrams. Consequently, those aids are of great help, but it must be kept in mind that the stability may be several per cent smaller.

7.2.2 **The magnitude of participating forces.** No serious concern arises with this problem if the right value of the unit weight is known. On the other hand, care is necessary when considering forces caused by seepage and pore water pressure or resulting from residual stress in the soil or rock mass.

Forces caused by seepage or by pore water pressure are in the simplest way considered as uplift forces. They are identical with the hydrostatic pressure on the surface that separates the body considered from the other mass. In the given case this surface is the slip surface. Therefore the uplift force is a force normal to the slip surface and the ordinate of its loading diagram at a given point equals the piezometric head. The problem is more complicated when compared with the current investigation of hydrostatic pressure, as the piezometric head at the given point does not equal its vertical distance from the water level. It is necessary to find the point of intersection of the equipotential line corresponding to the given point, with the water level. Therefore at least an approximate picture of the flow net is necessary.

For instance, in Fig. 7-1, the loading diagram of the uplift is drawn which acts on the area limited by points a_n and a_{n+1}. Ordinates of the loading diagram h equal the vertical distance of the points a from points a' defined as points of intersection of the equipotential lines Φ with the water level Ψ_o. By multiplying h_n by the unit weight of water, the magnitude of uplift u at the given point is defined. The total uplift force U_n can be obtained by multiplying the mean $^1/_2 (u_n + u_{n+1})$ by the length Δl_n. If pore water pressure has been measured or determined in other ways u is simply given by its magnitude.

The method as presented is preferable to other methods since it presents a clear conception of how the uplift invalidates the resistance of the mass along the slip surface. The effect of provisions to lower the water level or to reduce the pore water pressure can easily be judged.

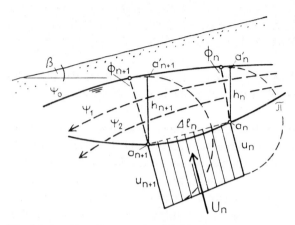

Fig. 7-1. Loading diagram of uplift U_n acting in sector a_n to a_{n+1} of the presumed slip surface; the value of uplift is given by flow and equipotential lines.

More difficult is the problem of how to apply the magnitude of residual forces existing in the mass in the stability analysis. This question remains open, as the influence of these forces upon the stability (sect. 2.3) has not been generally recognized. For the present time, at least, the impairment of the continuity of the mass appearing in the course of excavation should be considered (sect. 2.3). The impairment is due to deep cracks in the terrain outside the cutting and partial slip surfaces near the toe of the slopes. The cracks get filled with water and consequently the hydrostatic pressure acting on the walls should be introduced into the statical solution. The depth of these cracks is unknown in the given case. The analysis of the landslide at Bánovce (Mencl, 1965b) has shown that this depth is large, nearly equal to the height of the slope, when considering the shape and the backwards movement of the blocks as presented in Fig. 2-6b. Also the stability analysis of the mass after sliding suggested the possibility of the existence of large hydrostatic pressure since otherwise the rock resistance would have been very small. Not only rain-water, but also shallow underground water can fill the cracks. As long as provisions have been made to prevent the filling of cracks with water (e.g. by draining, pumping etc.), a lower water level can be considered for analysis.

The partial slip surfaces near the toe can form the foundation of the general slip surface. This question is dealt with in the subsequent paragraph.

7.2.3   **Problems of the strength of soils and rocks.** When resuming the conclusions arrived at in sections 2.3 and 6.5.3, two approaches result:

The method in which the peak value of strength is applied, is the most widespread one. But a relatively large safety factor is necessary to obtain a stable slope (sect. 7.2 and 7.2.4). As some portions of potential slip surface develop long before the slope collapses (as discussed in the preceding section), it is also possible to apply residual strength parameters φ'_R and c'_R (sect. 6.5.3) for these portions. This method takes into consideration the progressive failure, and the factor of safety may be smaller than with a peak value supposed as effective along the entire length of the slip surface. But always the strength parameters related to effective normal stress values, i.e. in considering the uplift or pore water pressure, should be applied.

The approach of several authors is quite contradictory (Gould, 1960). They recommend—supported by empirical findings—also applying strength para-

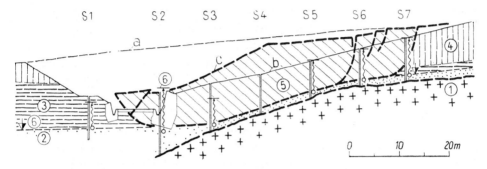

Fig. 7-2. Dependence of the stability of slope on the confined ground-water table; 1 — granite, 2 — Neogene sands, 3 — Neogene clay, 4 — loess loam, 5 — slid mass, 6 — confined water table, a — original slope surface, b — regraded slope surface, c — slope surface after the slide.

meters φ'_R and c'_R for slopes in undisturbed soils and associating them with a factor of safety, a little higher than unity. When existing slip surfaces interfere in the potential slip surface, the true angle of internal friction φ'_t is recommended.

Of the two possible approaches, the first one will be employed in the subsequent accounts. Residual strength is to be considered if distinct planes of discontinuity exist in the mass, e.g. old slip surfaces of ancient landslides or partial slip surfaces as discussed is sect. 2.3. The failure of the cutting in Neogene clays near Kuřim (Fig. 7-2)may be presented as an example. Here, the slip surface was predisposed by the basal plane of the Neogene clay. The underlying Neogene sand contained water under pressure. The partial slip planes near the toe likewise existed, as discussed in the sect. 2.2. Stability analysis yielded $\varphi' = 16$ degrees, i.e. equal to the value of φ'_R as recorded in Chapter 6.

The second method should be kept in view if progressive failure were expected. Nevertheless, with the exception of preliminary partial slip surfaces as discussed thoroughly in the preceding paragraphs, the question of progressive failure in clays remains open. Yet, the tendency to express, as best as possible, the

127

genuine development of failure by the statical solution, is to be welcomed. But in so far as the methods of such solutions are not defined in a satisfactory manner, the danger of potential failure will be compensated by a relatively high required factor of safety.

7.2.4   **The factor of safety.** The determination of the adequate factor of safety is a problem associated with a considerable responsibility. The position of the designer is not easy: on the one hand, he is responsible for the correct and safe design, on the other, he is expected to present economical solutions. He will often be criticized and told that his measures are insufficient, but hardly anybody will be willing to take the responsibility off his shoulders. But as soon as the danger is over and the excavation is completed, objections concerning the economy of the design will appear. Thus, a social factor is involved in his activity, namely, the duty to meet the requirements of society for both safety and economy. Moreover, the statical solution is undoubtedly only an idealized picture of reality and its perfection depends on the reliability of the investigated factors as well as on the adequacy of the geological cross-section of the slope.

The lack of a standard for the required minimum of safety factor, which would serve as a reliable basis to the designer, is a serious drawback. Consequently, apart from his own experience he takes over recommendations and comments from literature, which, however, often provides contradictory conceptions. In spite of this, a large majority of specialists agree that the factor of safety is the ratio of resisting forces (or of their moments) to the driving forces (or their moments) along the cross-section of the slip surface.

This relatively simple definition leads to intricate interpretations if the slope is supported by walls. Several solutions are possible according to the expected contribution of the given structural element to the stability of the slope and structure as a unit. The apparently simple requirement that the safety factor of both elements should be identical, is wrong. Foundations of walls are subjected to large concentrated stresses and therefore the danger of yielding, creep movements, fatigue or progressive failure, is greater than with slopes where a large area of the slip surface resists. Consequently, the opinion prevails that a smaller factor of safety may be attributed to the slope than to the supporting wall. The difference between the two safety factors approximates roughly a unity. For instance, when the required factor of safety of the foundations of the wall equals about 2.5, that of the slope equals about 1.5.

The structural limit state design theory has enriched the problem of the factor of safety with new aspects.

One of the principles of this approach consists in separating the factors incorporated till now in a unique general factor of safety. The partial factors are then attached to the members of the statical solution with which they are connected by their origin. Thus, e.g. the application of the uncertainty in the

128

determination of strength is not transferred till to the end of the solution, but appears right in the correction of the magnitude of strength.

This apparently simple rule, however, also presents several problems. They appear when enumerating the factors accounting for corrections and when trying to range them to the corresponding members, listed below:

(a) The strength of rocks and soils:
— The uncertainty in the determination of strength in view of the limited number of tests and the scattering of their results;
— the necessary reduction of peak value of strength as determined by standard tests with regard to the fact that long-term strength is smaller than that determined by short-term tests.
(b) The external forces: the uncertainty in their magnitude.
(c) The statical solution: the uncertainty as to whether the solution correctly represents the real interplay of forces. This correction should especially eliminate the danger of development of first cracks, of secondary slip surfaces, etc.
(d) The result: the safety in the proper sense giving rise to a safety factor necessary if an occasion should arise in which all the unexpected conditions — as outlined in (a) to (c) — might really occur. The factor of safety depends on the social importance of the structure, especially on the danger of loss of lives and property which would result from the collapse. This safety factor in the narrow sense need not be large and a magnitude of 1.1 to 1.25 is usually sufficient.

An apparently simple solution would consist in incorporating the corrections of (a) with the strength parameters, those of (b) with the unit weight; a simple solution for (c) and (d) consists in dividing the result of the statical solution by a factor. But, let us assume the problem of design of a retaining wall in clay, subjected to active earth pressure under the conditions that the strength of soil has been reduced by the factor (a) and the unit weight increased by factor (b). Factors (c) and (d) are assumed to be introduced after the numerical computation of the earth pressure has been done. But with cohesive soils, a case may arise, in which the equilibrium conditions will yield a negative value of earth pressure, i.e. in which the wedge of soil mass has very small stability without being supported by the wall. Consequently, we cannot increase the magnitude of earth pressure with respect to the factors (c) and (d).

By means of a simple analysis we can find that this danger does not exist with problems of stability of soil mass when it is supporting the structure (e.g. with the problem of bearing capacity of foundation soil in the case of a retaining wall). Consequently, two methods are possible:

Use is made of the procedure prerequisite for the active earth pressure analysis. With this the factor (b) is to be introduced by increasing the unit weight of the soil mass, while the factors (a), (c) and (d) are introduced by reducing the strength parameters. The result of the computation does not need correction any more. This system was preferred in the discussions at the International Conference on Soil Mechanics and Foundation Engineering in 1965. The factors (a), (c) and (d) usually result in a unique factor of about 1.6 with problems of the stability of slopes in cohesive soils. The parameters $\tan \varphi'$ and c' are divided by this factor and the required factor of safety is then $F = 1$.

The second method is to apply the above procedure only to the problems of earth pressure and of the stability of slopes. For the other problems, the method introducing the factors (c), (d) only in the end is used. This system was accepted in principle by the Committee for research in foundation engineering of COME-CON (Council for Mutual Economic Aid).

As discussed in sect. 7.2.3 the tendency prevails to decrease the reduction factors by endeavouring for a more realistic analysis.

7.2.5   **The stability analysis (in the narrow sense).** The design of the shape of slopes in undisturbed soils is more complex as the position of the potential slip surface is unknown. But several analytical methods are available and also the employment of computers is of great help. Both these approaches have a drawback in that the direct participation of the designer in the progress of computation is lost. The experience gained in the course of computation should not be neglected. Many engineers declare the statical computation of the stability of slopes to be a mechanical, tedious work. But this is true only for those who regard such computation as a sequence of figures and not a means towards knowledge. Intuition is necessary in the engineering geological profession and it cannot be gained without effort. By observing how the preponderance of the driving forces in the top part gradually recedes to the resistive forces when passing downwards along the slip surface, we can get a clear picture of the mechanism of the case. The significance of the shape of the slope surface, the effect of the corrective measures etc. will appear in their full extent.

On the other hand, complicated numerical computations are not necessary with simple problems. Consequently, two categories of problems should be distinguished:

A. *Slopes in simple conditions of homogeneous soils or rocks.* Statical analysis can be facilitated by the use of diagrams and tables. Those set up by Bishop and Morgenstern (1960) are the most widespread at the present time. They are based on Bishop's method of solution. But this method emphasizes the resistance of the soil mass at the toe of a slope produced by the rising section of the slip surface. As the strength of soils is generally reduced by swelling and by water seepage forces near the toe, the stability is a little smaller. Therefore the inclinations of slopes as indicated in table on the page 131 do not agree fully

130

with the results of Bishop's method. The table was set up for the purpose of a general view and contains gradients of slopes with the safety factor $F = 1$.

The data show the significance of cohesion for the stability and consequently the delicacy with which it is to be determined.

H (m)	c (kpcm^{-2})	φ			
		10°	15°	20°	25°
5	0.1	1.25	0.84	0.62	0.4
		1.9	1.22	0.9	0.7
10	0.1	2.3	1.7	1.35	0.9
		3.75	2.5	1.75	1.45
	0.2	1.25	0.84	0.62	0.4
		1.9	1.22	1	0.75
	0.3	0.53	0.34		
		0.85	0.6		
15	0.1	3.2	2.1	1.8	1.25
		5.2	3.6	2.4	1.75
	0.2	1.9	1.3	0.97	0.7
		2.9	1.95	1.25	1.3
	0.3	1.25	0.84	0.62	0.4
		1.9	1.22	1	0.8
20	0.1	3.5	2.25	1.85	1.35
		5.5	3.75	2.5	1.9
	0.2	2.3	1.7	1.35	0.9
		3.75	2.5	1.75	1.45
	0.3	1.9	1.15	0.81	0.62
		3	1.7	1.1	1

The value of m indicates the gradient as defined by the ratio 1 in m. The upper lines relate to the slope without water level, the lower ones to the slope with water level as shown in Fig. 7-3.

B. *Complex solutions.* When the surface of the slope is not straight and when the geological conditions are complex

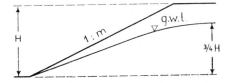

Fig. 7-3. Schematic cross-section of a slope with ground-water level to explain the above table.

and the slip surface cuts materials with differing properties, an individual solution is necessary. When choosing the method of analysis some care must be exercised. The perfect solution considering all statical conditions would be very laborious and because of statical renundancy also theoretically complex. Therefore the solutions have been simplified by neglecting several elements.

Care must be taken, of course, not to apply a method that neglects elements of importance for the given case or emphasizes those elements which either do not exist or are unreliable.

The objective of the solutions is to design a stable slope. As discussed in sect. 7.2, the interplay of driving and resistive forces as exists in the state of limit plastic equilibrium, is investigated. Since the design includes necessary corrections in order to be on the safe side, the analysis does not represent the real statical conditions of the slope as they will exist after construction.

7.2.6 Pettersson's Method.

The procedure of this method is known and does not need any explanation. It is based on the assumption that the normal stress, acting on the slip surface and giving rise to resistance, is produced only by the weight of the overburden existing directly over the given point. (Fig. 7-4a).

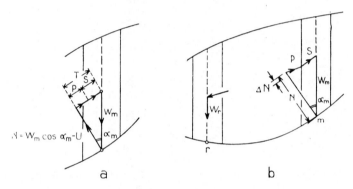

Fig. 7-4. Equilibrium of forces acting on a slice in stability computation. The load of slice W is resolved into normal W cos α and tangential T components. Normal component W cos α is often reduced by uplift U. As the resistance S of the upper slice (fig. a) on the slip surface is not large enough to overcome the shear component T, force P, which is produced by lower slices, is necessary. Petterson's analysis (fig. a) is based on the presumption that force N is not affected by force P. Fig. b shows that this assumption is not quite correct, as force T need not be perpendicular to N and thus alters normal force W cos α.

There is no doubt that this assumption does not hold true as the upper section of the slope is supported by the lower one. Consequently, when assuming in a schematic way that the slice m is partially supported by the slice r (Fig. 7-4b), the force acting between the two slices affects the magnitudes of N_m and N_r.

From this a conclusion can be drawn that the assumptions of Pettersson's method are not far from reality when the angles of the potential slip surface at its individual points do not differ. This is valid when its curvature is small. Therefore, its application is of advantage with sheet landslides on flat gentle slopes.

The solution yields the result:

$$F = \frac{\Sigma \, (W \cos \alpha - U) \tan \varphi' + \Sigma c' \varDelta l}{\Sigma W \sin \alpha}$$

where U denotes the uplift force (sect. 7.2.2). As U is subtracted from $W \cos \alpha$, parameters of strength $\tan \varphi'$ and c' are indeed those for effective normal stress values.

7.2.7   Bishop's Method. If the angle of a connecting line of two points of the slip surface differs considerably from the angles of the latter at those points,

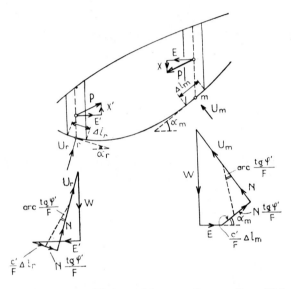

Fig. 7-5. Statical diagram of the equilibrium of forces acting on slices (Bishop's analysis). For clearness sake simplified to the collaboration of two slices (m and r).

Pettersson's solution is not suitable. Bishop (1955) emphasizes in his simplified solution the importance of the horizontal components of forces P, i.e. of the forces E. The vertical components are neglected. Fig. 7-5 shows that the component E augments the resistance at the base of the upper slices (e.g. of the slice m), as it increases N forces. On the other hand, with the lower slice, N is increased only when the slip surface ascends near the toe (the slice r). But N is reduced due to E in the descending section of the surface near the toe. Therefore, the importance of the increase in resisting forces due to the ascending section of the surface is emphasized in this solution. But even in that section of the mass the material is often weakened by swelling and seepage. Consequently, it is necessary not to overestimate this component of resistance.

The analysis yields a formula:

$$F = \frac{1}{\Sigma W \sin \alpha} \sum \frac{(W - U \cos \alpha) \tan \varphi' + c' \Delta l \cos \alpha}{\cos \alpha + \sin \alpha \dfrac{\tan \varphi'}{F}}$$

As F is also implicitly contained on the right side of this expression an approximate solution is necessary (e.g. by using Pettersson's method) and the resulting value of F is inserted into the formula.

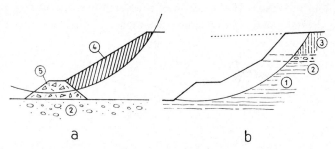

Fig. 7-6. The suitable shape of slopes for the analysis of stability according to Fig. 7-7; 1 — Neogene clay, 2 — sandy gravel, 3 — loess loam, 4 — fill, 5 — rubble backfill.

When the force X is also to be introduced into the statical analysis, i.e. when the entire force P is to be considered, the solution is possible only when some assumptions are tolerated, concerning the direction of the force P. Thus, Mencl and Němcová (1965) assumed that the forces P are parallel to the tangents of the slip surface at the given points. This solution is therefore suitable for rather concave shapes of slopes as are the slopes presented by Fig. 7-6.

Also with this method the approximate value of F must be known. The principle of the solution is shown by Figs. 7-7 and 7-8. They illustrate how the

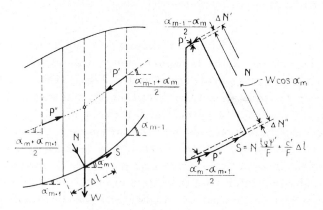

Fig. 7-7. Forces acting on slice, statical solution according to Mencl and Němcová (1956).

134

forces P' and P'' augment the normal force N and in this way also the resistance. The increase in N is given by:

$$\Delta N = \Delta N' + \Delta N'' = P' \frac{\alpha_{m-1} - \alpha_m}{2} + P'' \frac{\alpha_m - \alpha_{m+1}}{2}$$

The forces P'' can be computed from the simplified polygon of forces (Fig. 7-8):

$$P'' = P' + W \sin \alpha - W \cos \alpha \frac{\tan \varphi'}{F} - \frac{c'}{F} \Delta l$$

Then:

$$F = \frac{\Sigma(N + \Delta N) \tan \varphi' + \Sigma c' \Delta l}{\Sigma T}$$

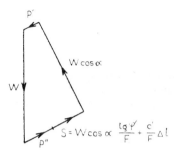

This method gives higher factor of safety as compared with Bishop's method under conditions that the slip surface does not contain an ascending section and that the toe of the slope contains materials with larger strength (a gravel layer, a sheet of debris etc.). This also demonstrates the large statical importance of a rubblework at the toe (Fig. 7-6a).

Fig. 7-8. Simplified scheme to Fig. 7-7.

7.3 Stability of sliding slopes

This problem is relatively simple. The fact that the factor of safety of a sliding slope equals unity as well as the possibility to determine the position of the slip surface is very informative.

Safety factors of sliding slopes are nearly equal to unity. With the safety factor of about 0.95, a rapid movement occurs in cohesive soils. Consequently the values between 0.96 and 1 can be discussed and it is often safer to assume a smaller value than unity.

The shape of the slip surface often differs from the arc. As the continuity of the mass is often invalidated by the movement, Pettersson's method of analysis is generally suitable. In Fig. 7-9 the cross-section of the sliding slope in the flysch rocks near Bludovice, Moravia is shown. The solution yields the value of $\varphi' = 19$ degrees which is characteristic of loamy debris involved in the landslide.

As the factors of uncertainty are reduced, only the true factor of safety (as denoted by d in sect. 7.2.4) is necessary. As stated above, this is of the order of 1.1 to 1.25. Nevertheless, the value of 1.1 is too small, as the other factors are not fully eliminated. The factor of safety of the stabilized landslide should decrease under 1.15 only if there is a special reason (e.g. that the stability will increase with time etc.).

One of the most stabilizing measures is the drainage of ground water. Landslides produced by uplift occur on slopes with small gradients (about 12 to 14 degrees). Therefore it is not necessary to draw a flow net for the determination of uplift head. Equipotential lines can be represented by vertical straight lines and the uplift head is defined by the elevation of the water table over the given

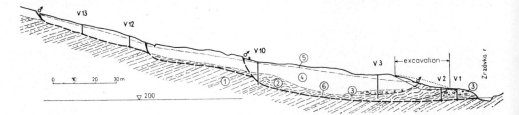

Fig. 7-9. Diagrammatic section of the Bludovice slide area near Nový Jičín in Moravia (Mencl, 1966a); 1 — marly shales, 2 — moulded marly shales, 3 — sandy gravel, 4 — slope loam with sandstone fragments, 5 — ground-water level, 6 — presumed slip surface.

point. Exceptions from this simple rule occur with layers of differing permeability. Landslides in this case tend to occur rather along the contact plane of the less permeable layer with the underlying, (Fig. 7-2) more permeable one. The uplift is to be measured directly by boreholes which work as piezometric tubes.

In the preceding paragraph the most frequent mechanism of landslides was considered by assuming that the soil or rock mass has been disintegrated by movement. Therefore Pettersson's method was recommended. Nevertheless, with rock masses and with the early stage of the failure another mechanism develops. The rock slides along bedding planes belong to this category. After

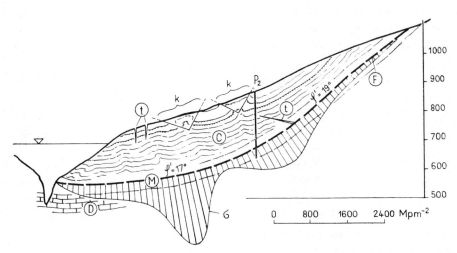

Fig. 7-10. Diagrammatic section of the Monte Toc slope close before collapse; D — flaggy limestones, Dogger, M — marly limestones, Malm, F — slip plane, C — marly limestones, Lower Cretaceous, k — squeezed out rock wedges, t — tension joints (after Mencl, 1966c).

the sliding movement has begun, it can be hindered and even prevented by the stiffness of the sliding mass as soon as the rock mass has slid from the more straight section of the slip surface into the more curved one. Unless the sliding mass disintegrates, a redistribution of pressures appears and this is to be considered in the statical solution (Mencl, 1966c).

As an example, the rock slide of Monte Toc into the reservoir of Vaiont in the stage before collapse can be cited. The working hypothesis of this landslide is presented in Fig. 7-10. As long as the sliding mass did not break by the rise of tensile cracks (t) at the base and by squeezing out a wedge (k) in the upper compressed section, the redistribution of forces on the sliding surface increased. Owing to the stiffness of the sliding mass the compression forces were concentrated in the upper and lower sections of the sliding surface. Figure 7-10 presents the approximative distribution of the normal stress σ along the slip surface.

When assuming the setting down of the mass at the beginning of the movement, Pettersson's method yields $\varphi = 20$ degrees for $F = 1$. After the redistribution occurred, $\varphi = 18$ degrees was sufficient for $F = 1$. Consequently, the movement of the landslide changed into a creep and in several periods it even stopped. As soon as the rock mass had disintegrated, the acceleration of the movement resulted. When examining the outcrops of strata on the surface of the slid body, as established by Selli and Trevisan (1964), it can be assumed that processes of the same kind had occurred at least once in the past.

Chapter 8

CORRECTIVE MEASURES

8.1   **Schedule of stabilization works**

The stabilization of landslides must be executed out according to a well-thought-out plan, which lists the individual tasks in order of urgency. It would be wrong, for instance, to plan extensive earthworks for the slope adjustment prior to the drainage of surface waters, because the redeposited soil would again be soaked by water. The first remedial measures should include:

(a) Capture and drainage of surface water flowing into the slide area or issuing in the head scarp.

(b) Pumping of water from all wells in the slide area and dewatering of drainless depressions.

(c) Filling and tamping of all open cracks which could be pervaded by surface water. This concerns particularly deep cracks developed during slope movement which reach up to the slide plane, thus enabling a deep penetration of the water. The cracks may be even filled with material from the vicinity, but it should be done as soon after the temporary cessation of movement as possible. The filling of cracks is often neglected to the detriment of stability, as surface and rain water in soaking into the loosened material exerts hydrostatic and uplift pressure and thus impairs the physical properties of rocks.

Only after this stage of remedial measures should the slide be drained by subsurface pipes, galleries or horizontal borings and can the readjustment of the ground surface according to a plan based on detailed investigation be carried out.

The schedule of corrective measures must pay due regard to climatic conditions. In Central Europe extensive works are very difficult or even impossible in winter or spring, as the surface of the waterlogged slide area is not easily accessible. The dates of partial corrective works must be given due consideration and carefully observed so as not to interfere seriously with the effect of treatment. In some cases it is more correct to abstain from any corrective works than to leave them unfinished.

In many slide areas the slope movements repeat periodically in climatically adverse seasons. Therefore, all corrective devices must be regularly checked and maintained. When the maintenance of controlling structures in regular intervals is not ensured, or the regime appointed for the usage of the slide area is not observed, even extensive and costly corrective measures may be depreciated within a very short period.

8.2   Treatment of the slope shape

The stability of the slope may be substantially increased either by reducing the load of soil at the head or by its enlargement at the toe of the landslide. If, for instance, approximately four per cent of the slipping-mass volume is displaced from the head to the toe of the slope, its stability increases by ten per cent. This method of correction is recently preferred as no laborious masonry and concreting works are needed.

Another advantage of this procedure is in that it can generally be started, without previous time-consuming research work.

However, the excavated soil from the top part of the landslide frequently cannot be used for loading the toe, as for instance, in loamy soils. In this case it is more suitable to bring the material from another locality and to deposit the excavated soil on a dump. The surcharge of the toe proves effective when the dip of the slide plane at the head (where the material would be excavated) is less than 40° and when the substratum of the loading embankment is drained. In town areas, material from foundation excavations, rubble or ash may be used for the loading of the toe of the downslipping slope. If, as is often the case, the drainage of the subsoil of the loading fill is neglected, this actually adds to the volume of the sliding mass and becomes part of the landslide. Such incorrect procedure caused unjustifiable distrust of this treatment.

The landslide toe cannot be loaded, as a rule, in the cuttings of communications and canals and the slope movement should be stopped by unloading the upper part. It is, however, always necessary to examine whether or not the loading of the toe is really impossible. In some railway cuttings (for instance, on the line Brno—Břeclav) a slight change of the gradient of the track (i.e. the subgrade in the cuttings) made the use of a loading fill possible. It is well known that small, so-called "lost" gradients do not increase operational costs and frequently contribute to a better drainage of the cuttings. Such gradient modifications cannot be carried out in the bends of highroads and another method must be sought.

The unloading of the head is usually least expensive, its costs depending on the accessibility of the slope. If the access of vehicles is possible, it is cheapest to move the soil downslope where it may serve as a permanent or temporary load. When, however, the rocks in the upper part of the slide are waterlogged or broken into blocks, transport is far more difficult: the construction of a provisory access road with a solid pavement is expensive and the excavation of rock mass is aggravated. In removing material from the head scarp, care must be

Fig. 8-1. Handlová landslide, 1961. Provisional diversion of water carried out by means of ventilation pipes and fire-hoses (photograph by Bárta).

taken not to disturb the equilibrium of the upper part of the slope which could result in the enlargement of the landslide.

The treatment of the slope shape should be designed simultaneously with the subdrainage, as the drainage decreases the volume of earthwork needed for the stabilization of the slope. Sometimes further earthworks can even be discontinued which proves advantageous particularly in winter months when frozen soil is difficult to excavate but subdrainage can be installed.

For the time being it is not recommendable to design slopes in soils steeper than 1 : 2, because slopes inclined at a greater angle cannot be graded mechanically.

8.3   Drainage of landslides

8.3.1   **Surface drainage.** The surface of the area affected by sliding is generally uneven, hummocky and traversed by deep fissures. In depressions and fissures water accumulates and wet grounds develop. Therefore, one of the first remedial measures is the surface drainage of the slide area. Although surface drainage in itself is seldom sufficient for the stabilization of a slope in motion, it can contribute substantially to the drying and thus also, controlling of the landslide.

140

Fig. 8-2. Handlová landslide; drainage ditches paved by concrete tiles. A step-like arrangement of the ditch enables the drainage of water infiltrated into the sand bed (photograph by Záruba).

First, all streams and temporary watercourses should be prevented from entering the threatened area. In addition, all springs issuing within the slide area, especially at its head, must be entrapped and diverted outside the slide. For the immediate provisional diversion of water any pipes available may be used. Surface waters on the Handlová landslide were drained off by means of air pipes lent by the Handlová Mine and by fire-hoses (Fig. 8-1). In the first stage of sliding, when the movement and the changes of relief are appreciable, the surface pipes are advantageous, as their displacement is easy and inexpensive. In winter, however, they prove less suitable because they do not protect water from freezing.

After a partial stabilization of the landslide, open ditches of adequate dimensions and gradient are excavated for discharging rain water. At the same time, the ground surface should be levelled out and drainless depressions and all cracks filled so as to ensure a continuous run-off of surface water. During this treatment the grass cover should not be disturbed unnecessarily, as it decreases the possibility of water percolation into the slope.

The arrangement of ditches depends on the type of soil; their banks and bottom

Fig. 8-3. Handlová landslide; permanent maintenance of the paving is necessary as even small movements disturb the ditch which loses its function.

must be sufficiently firm and resistant to erosion. They are paved either by natural stone of suitable properties, or by concrete tiles set into a sand bed and the joints are sealed by cement mixture or sod. Water infiltrating into the sand bed is drained into the ditch by establishing a low step (Fig. 8-2). In sandy soils, ditch walls and bottom may be consolidated by asphalt, bitumen or oil sprinkle.

In some cases ditch tiles of reinforced concrete proved suitable for surface drainage. They are slightly narrowed at one end so that they can be inserted telescopically into one another. Compared with paving, gutters of reinforced concrete are advantageous in being less pervious; owing to their position in a yielding environment, they withstand even slight movement of the slope without damage. Wooden troughs, which are occasionally used, can be easily set together and redeposited, but by frequent moistening and drying out wood deteriorates and loses its imperviousness.

In addition to ditches constructed in the slide area, peripheral ditches above the head scarp are sometimes excavated for diverting the surface water flowing down the adjacent slopes into the potentially unstable area. These peripheral ditches require permanent, thorough maintenance because otherwise they

142

may contribute to the extension of the slide area. They must be provided with impervious paving and have a uniform gradient so as to avoid filling by washed material in flatter sections. Water ponded in blocked ditches causes additional disturbance of the slope and may seriously injure the stability even of a slide which is temporarily at rest.

8.3.2 **Subsurface drainage.** In paragraph 2.3 the effect of uplift and of forces developed by ground-water flow on the origin of landslides was shown.

As the ground water is one of the major causes of slope instability, the subsurface drainage is a very effective remedial measure. It complements or substitutes the adjustement of slopes, because a drained slope may by stable at a steeper angle than an undrained one. The disadvantage of subdrainage consists in that it can be designed only after geological and hydrogeological research has been completed so that it enters into operation somewhat belatedly.

Vertical exploration borings arranged as pumping wells are free of such a disadvantage. The diameter of the borings, however, must be larger than that of the exploration holes because the diameter of the casing for the pumps must be at least 219 mm, which, even if the width of the filtration backfill is minimum, increases the hole diameter to 280—300 mm. The progress of borings is thus slower and the investigation of the area is retarded, but every completed boring represents an effective pumping well.

If old water wells exist at the locality, they should immediately be exhausted. They are often provided with pumps and the inhabitants may be persuaded to empty them in their own interest. Where the water rises near to the surface, the pumps of the fire brigade prove convenient, as they are easily transportable, highly effective and driven by a petrol engine. With the increasing density of the exploration and pumping hole network the picture of geological, geotechnical and hydrogeological conditions of the area becomes clearer and precise enough so as to serve as a basis for the proposal of definitive drainage measures. These include the use of drainage galleries and horizontal drainage borings.

Drainage galleries are conventional deep structures such as were used in the first railway constructions in the last century. They are advantageous in several ways. They serve as a means for the exploration of water percolation in the rock and thus help to solve precisely the hydrogeological conditions of the slope. Owing to their large perimeter, a large amount of water may be discharged; their effectiveness may be increased by short or longer drainage borings in the walls, floor or roof of the gallery. Thus, they can be constructed even below the slide plane and gather water from the overlying layers by vertical boreholes. If the water seems to run from the more permeable bed in the floor of the gallery, a shaft or a trench may be excavated in its floor. The course of the gallery may be changed so as to follow the influx of water or to reach the bottom of vertical

Fig. 8-4. Boring of horizontal drainage holes with the use of boring device of A. Wirth & Co., Erkelenz, Rheinland.

drainage boreholes. The diameter of galleries is generally so large that they discharge the water even when partly disturbed.

Yet, they have several disadvantages, too: first, they are costly, because the drainage of several litres per second requires the construction of a large engineering work. The effectiveness of drainage galleries is sometimes criticized unjustifiably by laymen who expect that an "underground lake" will be tapped. The driving of galleries in disturbed slid rocks is laborious and may be threatened by caving. The use of mechanization means for loading and transport which are applied nowadays to lower the excavation cost, results, on the other hand, in the increased dimensions of galleries and thus also in a higher cost of the fill. Drainage galleries should not remain hollow; they are backfilled with stone or gravel to ensure their drainage capacity even at a partial deformation. The backfilling is very expensive manual work.

In spite of these disadvantages, galleries still represent an indispensable method where the drainage of deep slides has to be performed over a length of 200 m, which is so far the extreme length attainable for drainage borings in soft rocks. The use of these galleries for the stabilization of the Handlová landslide is shown in Fig. 5-15.

Drainage borings are at least five times cheaper than drainage galleries. The cost is also lowered by the shorter period needed for their construction,

144

provided suitable machinery is available, and by the reduction of pumping works from temporary vertical wells. There are two drawbacks to drainage borings: (a) it is dificult to guarantee that they hit the water-bearing beds in which the pressure of ground water impairs the stability of the slide; (b) the length of borings capable of performance at present does not exceed 200 m, so that their effectiveness in extensive landslides cannot be ensured.

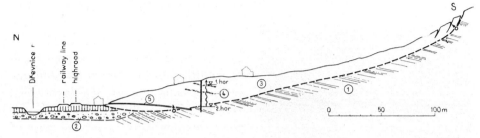

Fig. 8-5. Cross-section of a landslide at Příluky near Gottwaldov (Moravia). Total movement between 1961—1963 was about 1.5 m, most houses were disturbed. Three horizontal drainage borings reaching into the bedrock discharge 169 litres/min. 1 — Palaeogene sandstones and shales, 2 — sandy gravels, 3 — slid slope-loam and detritus, 4 — humic loam, 5 — drainage borings.

Short drainage borings in low slopes are performed by driving perforated pipes into the slope; in railway cuttings, discarded engine pipes have often been used. This procedure proves suitable where the aquifers are comparatively thin sand or gravel beds.

Long horizontal drainage borings are carried out by the following two methods:

(a) The drilling of long holes by helical augers; perforated pipes are driven into the holes made (Fig. 8-4).

(b) Rotary drilling by cutter and roller bits. Perforated drill pipes serve simultaneously as permanent casing. In the course of drilling the walls of the holes are stabilized by drilling mud. This procedure has been developed by the Geological Research at Jihlava (Jedlička and Tkaný, 1965; Mencl, 1965b) and has been applied successfully in several cases. The maximum length of 206 m was attained. At Příluky near Gottwaldov, in sliding flysch rocks the discharge of three horizontal drainage borings 80—100 m long and 108 mm in diameter, which reach into the bedrock, is 169 litres/min (Figs. 8-5, 8-6). The drawback of this procedure is that the bit remains in the hole.

The technique described requires the use of pipes with walls of a sufficient thickness (6 mm with an inner diameter of 83 mm), because thinner pipes are deformed by torsion. It is advisable to drill the hole at a gentle angle upslope; frost does not penetrate inside and the water does not freeze at the mouth of the hole. In designing a horizontal boring it must be borne in mind that the hole is bent down by the weight of the drill pipes, so that the end of a 60 m long bore is two to three metres lower than proposed.

145

In some cases borings carried out at the foot of the slopes (from the bottom of cuttings) are not sufficient for the control of the slide. If water issues at several levels, additional borings must also be performed higher up so as to drain all ground-water horizons.

Drainage trenches. In the past, and occasionally even at present, slopes were drained by a network of trenches. These sometimes had to be very deep and as their construction was not easy they were not always sunk to the necessary depth, so that the drainage was incomplete and the slide movement continued. In addition to exacting work and the great consumption of timber for bracing, trenches in poorly consolidated soils were threatened by caving. Because of a long building period, they were sometimes damaged before completion. The excavation of trenches advanced from the lower end upwards to make possible the continuous discharge of water during the work, but this procedure led to the silting of the lower part by material washed down the slope. The need to excavate the whole length of the trench before backfilling, which was supposed to prevent this trouble, resulted in turn in the lengthening of the building period. For these reasons, drainage trenches nowadays recede to horizontal borings or galleries.

Fig. 8-6. Horizontal drainage boring, 78 m long, discharges 86 litres/min. (Příluky land-slide, photograph by Tkaný).

On the other hand, trenches constructed in the slopes of cuttings or cut-offs are still a suitable measure for concentrating the water outflow and thus preventing its entrance into the slope. Trenches should reach beyond the depth of frost action. They are protected from freezing by a sodded humus cover. Humus is underlaid by a protective layer (brushwood, reed, foils of synthetic material) to prevent the silting of the trench fill, which is generally gravel.

The design of drainage trenches should be based on a sound knowledge of the geological and hydrogeological conditions of the slope in order not to impair its stability during excavation. In glaciofluvial deposits in the Ostrava area, sand beds alternate with sandy clays on which ground water is retained. In this case drainage trenches must be provided with an impermeable bottom, because otherwise, puncturing the impermeable clay bed would result in emptying the

146

water into a lower horizon and thus possibly in another slide on a deeper clay bed (Fig. 8-7).

At present, trenches are often excavated as broad troughs by means of a bulldozer instead of by laborious hand digging and casing. The consumption of gravel for the fill is, naturally, larger, but so is the effectiveness of the trenches. When at the toe of the slide the slushed soil has to be removed concurrently with the filling of the space by gravel, a power shovel is applied. Successful stabilization

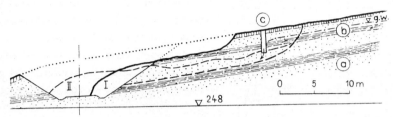

Fig. 8-7. The piercing of impermeable clay bed by drainage trench resulted in the discharge of water into a lower horizon and thus in a new landslide (II.) on the lower clay bed; a — glacio-fluvial sands, b — clay, c — drainage trench.

of the landslide by this technique also depends to a great extent on the promptness of all workers. Sometimes it is necessary to construct a temporary gravel buttress at the toe of the slide for successive trenches to abut against it.

8.4   Stabilization of landslides by vegetation

Slope movements generally disturb the vegetation cover, including both tree growth and grass mat. The reforestation of the slope is an important task of corrective treatment; it is carried out during its last stage, invariably after at least partial stabilization of the landslide. The planting of forest trees is preceded by drainage of the area, levelling of the surface and tamping of cracks. Afforestation, however, is a promising method only for shallow sheet slides. Landslides with deep-lying slide planes cannot be detained by vegetation, although in this case, too, it can partly lower the infiltration of surface water into the slope and thus contribute indirectly to the stabilization of the slide.

It is generally accepted that the forest growth has two functions: drying out of the surface layers and their consolidation by a network of roots. As trees draw the water necessary for their growth from surface beds, the most suitable ones for planting on sliding slopes would be those that have the largest consumption of water and highest evaporation. Therefore, it is more advantageous to plant deciduous trees (alders, poplars, willows, ash-trees, birches, Skatula, 1953) than conifers which exhibit comparatively the lowest evaporation.

Sýkora (1961), who systematically studied the influence of vegetation on sliding movements, mentions that in selecting suitable trees for sliding slopes, their effects on the structure of soil should also be taken into consideration. For this reason, spruces should not be planted, which, moreover, have only shallow roots and by their relatively rapid growth increase the loading of the slope.

The above-mentioned author recommends first sowing suitable kinds of grass, herbs and hedges and only afterwards trees. According to the results of this investigation, the main type of indigenous forest on Czechoslovak slide areas are oaks with hornbeams. He recommends planting oaks mixed with hornbeams, ashtrees, alders, willows, poplars and aspens.

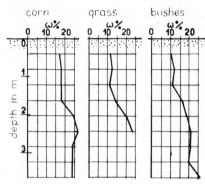

Fig. 8-8. Water content of clayey soil is diminished to a depth of 2.5 m beneath the grassy surface; the influence of bushes reaches deeper than 3 m (Felt, 1953).

Experience has shown that a mixed forest and a gradual rejuvenation of growth is most convenient on the slides. Extensive clear felling should be avoided, because it disturbs the stability of the slope as a result of the change in the surface and ground water system; if the surface is affected by erosion, the possibility of the infiltration of surface water is greatly increased. The infiltration is also facilitated when the slide area is used as a pasture land; the cattle tears up the grass cover and injures surface drainage, growing bushes and trees.

The significance of vegetation for the stabilization of sheet slides is often underrated. Yet it should be borne in mind that grass cover not only prevents drying of the surface and the formation of shrinkage cracks but removes water directly from the top layers. The measurement of the humidity in clayey soils carried out by Felt (1953) has shown that below grassy areas (Fig. 8-8) humidity is reduced to a depth of about 2.5 m and the influence of bushes reaches deeper than 3 metres.

8.5   Retaining walls and similar structures

Retaining walls are occasionally erected to increase the stability of slopes or to consolidate existing landslides. Their application is often occasioned either by the lack of space necessary for the development of the slope to a full length, or by the landslide close to a track in railway cuts. As retaining walls are subjected to an unfavourable system of loading, a large wall width is necessary to increase the stability of the slope. Therefore, the application of walls appears uneconomical and is often subjected to discussions. Their construction also requires a great deal of manual and skilled work, expensive formwork and transport facility in the unifinished cutting.

148

In spite of it, the design with the use of a retaining wall is to be preferred (with respect to the stability of slope) in three cases:

(a) Low walls, supporting slopes in clayey soils to prevent loosening of the toe and to protect it from frost action.

(b) Low walls or other supports, fastening the toe of existing landslides.

(c) Large retaining walls, often braced in a particular manner, subjected to the full earth pressure, if no other design of a cutting is possible.

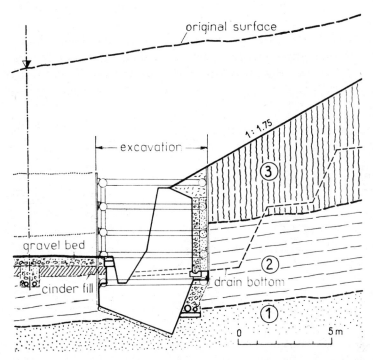

Fig. 8-9. Retaining walls proved suitable in deep cuttings; they are built successively in sectors in braced excavation trenches; 1 — waterlogged sands, 2 — Neogene clays, 3 — loess loam.

Retaining walls in the so-called fissured clay belong to the first category. Neogene clays in the ČSSR often show this form of secondary structure. Stiff clay and claystone layers contain systems of hair cracks, often with smoothly polished surfaces, which remain closed as long as the clay mass remains wet. During dry seasons the cracks open and rain-water penetrates into the mass. This results in slides, often even after a considerable time of rest. Several corrective measures are necessary, such as confining the toe of the slope to prevent its loosening, draining gravitational water out of the slope and covering the surface of the slope with humus soil and grass to prevent desiccation. The toe can be confined by a low wall, which has also the function of supporting rubble drains and directing the drained water either into the weep holes or into the longitudinal drains situated at the back of the wall. This protects the drained water from frost action before leaving the slope. The weep holes in the walls should be narrow (they can be constructed of drain-pipes of a diameter of about 8 centimeters) and inclined to the face of the wall to prevent penetration of icy air. As the footing of the wall needs a toe projection it was often tied with a concrete ditch (Fig. 8-9) in the past. Nowadays, any changes in the shape of the subgrade are to be avoided so as not to prevent use of mechanical equipment for ballast maintenance. Hence, the side ditches must not transgress into the width of the subgrade.

The function of the walls limiting the toe of existing landslides is somewhat different. Usually water escapes from the sliding mass and the soil becomes slushy. This decreases the resistance of the toe and the stability of the sliding

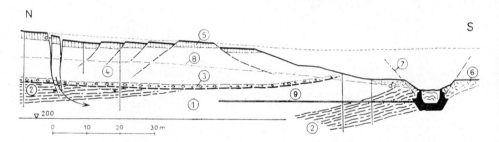

Fig. 8-10. Cross-section of the landslide in the railway cutting at Bánovce (Slovakia); 1 — sandstones and argillaceous shales, 2 — Palaeogene claystones, 3 — loamy gravels, 4 — Neogene clayey silts, 5 — loam, 6 — fill, 7 — surfaces limiting the wedge squeezed out into the cutting, 8 — ground-water table (after slope collapse) in borings sunk into Palaeogene sandstones, 9 — horizontal drainage borings (Mencl, 1965b).

mass. A low wall can prevent the loosening of the toe. If there is free space available it is better to construct the wall several meters in front of the toe and to fill the remaining space with gravel, thus forming a counter dam and a drain layer of the toe. In an opposite case, it is necessary to remove the material of the toe and to construct the wall in steps. A rubblework is more apt then as it permits the construction in sections and is suitable to carry the earth pressure within a short time. The rubblework toe is covered with gravel afterwards and serves as a longitudinal drain. It is necessary to stretch it out to maintain the longitudinal gradient needed to conduct drained water.

High, large retaining walls are expensive and therefore their statical solution requires special attention. The wall has to resist large horizontal forces, either in order to increase the stability of an intact slope or to support deep sliding mass. In both cases a nearly similar type of structure results, but the statical solutions differ. In the former case the wall has to resist the pressure at rest, which with the height of the wall h and with the gradient of slope 1 in 2.5 reaches

150

Fig. 8-11. View of the railway cutting at Bánovce with retaining walls (photograph by Tkaný)

the value of $S_0 = 1/2 \cdot 0.8\,\gamma\,h^2$ (γ is the unit weight of soil). Larger values of horizontal pressure can be encountered in clayey soil mass due to residual stress (sect. 2.3). In the cutting at Bánovce horizontal stress amounting to nearly 1.5 times the vertical pressure of the existing overburden was measured at the bottom in the section of the cutting not influenced by the sliding movement.

If the wall supports the toe of a deep landslide, the pressure may also considerably exceed the pressure at rest. As an example, the cut at Bánovce in the section of an existing large landslide may be quoted (Fig. 8-10). The value of about three-times the pressure at rest was ascertained, i.e. $S = 1/2 \ 2.4\,\gamma h^2$, by the statical computation of the stability of the wedge of claystone mass in the bottom of the cutting.

It is why it was necessary (Mencl, 1965b) to design walls monolitically tied to one another into an invert frame. The back of the wall was battered and provided with a small heel projection for two reasons: to avoid the necessity of bracing the excavation pit, and to increase the stability of the frames by the weight of the backfill. The frames were set up in sections 7 m long and it was necessary to construct them section after section. As soon as the length of excavation pit was enlarged over nearly three sections, the movement of the

Fig. 8-12. Concrete crib wall, according to F. Zitta's system.

sliding mass revived, in spite of the fact that the level of ground water was lowered down to the level of the top of the walls by means of 16 deep-well pumps. The surveying during the construction showed that the central section of the frame belt was shifted about 30 cm to the right. To replace the function of deep wells, 7 horizontal drainage boreholes were installed up to a length of 70 m. The total discharge amounts to 0.8 litres/sec.

It is evident that besides a large consumption of manual and skilled work, the use of retaining walls may be associated with the risk of slope failure. The demands of construction are aggravated additionally by the necessity of the constructions of walls in short sections, very often in shafts, and prior to the excavation of the cutting itself. As a result, the use of high walls should be limited to the cases where no other more suitable solution exists.

Some attention is to be given to the crib walls. They are constructed of precast reinforced concrete units (Fig. 8-12) set up in cells which are filled with gravel or stone. They are advantageous in that they afford a rapid erecting with the help of a mobile crane, and an easy adjustment to differential settlement as well as the statical effectiveness immediately after construction. It is why they replace to advantage concrete walls, but as supports of unstable slopes they can serve only in shallow sheet slides. Under the action of large forces the units break, especially in joints.

152

In particularly serious cases not even the monolitically compound walls are sufficient and it is necessary to construct a tunnel. Fig. 8-13 presents the solution adopted for the cutting of the railway Spaichingen-Nusplingen in Germany (Zeller, 1924). The side-hill cutting was designed at first across the deposits of Jurassic clays, marly limestones and sandstones with a thick coverage of slope debris. As soon as the excavation reached the level as shown by the dot-and-

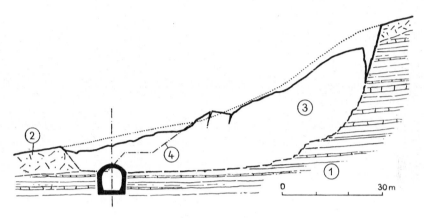

Fig. 8-13. Diagrammatic section of a backfilled vaulted cutting on the Spaichingen-Nusplingen railway line in Germany; 1 — marly limestones and sandstones, Jurassic, 2 — slope debris, 3 — slid mass, 4 — slope of the cutting before sliding (Zeller, 1924).

dashed line, the slope collapsed, buried the excavation and a deep crack opened at a distance of 60 m to the right. The slip surface developed along a nearly horizontal weak weathered layer of Jurassic clay. The design was changed and the backfilled vaulted cut was adopted. The construction of 21 tunnel sections each 7 m in length, took 21 months. They were constructed section after section in pits and the vaulted sections were backfilled immediately. Some sections were vaulted over only with reinforced concrete arches, and some were reinforced with steel trusses around the whole circumference.

Overbridging of the sliding area. In some cases it is more economical not to stabilize the slope but to lay out the road on a bridge spanning the dangerous area. This solution is expensive, but it was used several times on steep mountain slopes, especially over narrow earth flows.

The possibility of laying out the road on a bridge across the large sheet slides depends on the depth of the moving mass, and on the direction of the slope movement in relation to the road axis. With shallow sheet slides and with the stable rock at accessible depth, the piers can be constructed to support the bridge structure. The bridge piers must not hinder the free creep movement of the slope deposits. Fig. 8-14 presents a crossing of a mountain slope by a road used

153

Fig. 8-14. The bridging of the sliding area near the power plant Kaprun in the Austrian Alps (photograph by Záruba).

at the hydroenergetic plant of Kaprun in the Austrian Alps. The slope is covered with unstable rock debris. A similar solution was used at the diversion road along the reservoirs of the Morávka and Šance dams in the Beskydy Mountains.

8.6 Rock bolts

Stabilization of rock mass by means of rock bolts, which has found a widespread application in mining and tunnelling, has also become a method to prevent movement of rock slopes and sometimes to stabilize rock slides. Today it is also applied to the stabilization of soil slopes, as a rule, in connection with retaining structures. The three principal factors which come into consideration, when designing the system of bolts are the statical effect of bolts, its durability, and the time factor in the course of anchoring.

The statical effect of rock bolts results partly from the increase in normal forces acting on an existing or potential slip surface, and partly from the tangential component of the bolt forces. With the angle of inclination of the slope β (Fig. 8-15), the angle between the bolt axis and the normal to the slip surface α, and with the angle of shear resistance along the slip surface φ, the safety factor of the rock mass is given by:

$$F = \frac{(W \cos \beta + K \cos \alpha) \tan \varphi - K \sin \alpha}{W \sin \beta}$$

in which K is the total force in the rock bolts. Moreover two phenomena are to be considered when analysing the stability:

(a) The unfavourable influence of uplift and/or of hydrostatic pressure of water entering the fissures in the rock mass, as well as of the forces caused by water freezing in fissures. To prevent it the surface of the slope should be covered, the rock mass sealed with grouting and drained by means of inclined boreholes, etc.

(b) Phenomena of the relaxation of resistance of the rock mass. The relaxation phenomenon affects the interplay between the component $K \sin \alpha$, which is produced by the relatively stiff anchoring of the rock-bolt, and the component $(W \cos \beta + K \cos \alpha) \tan \varphi$ which is induced by the rather weak shear resistance of the rock. As mentioned in sect. 8.5, in the co-operation of a stiff support, and of a weak shear resistance of the rock, the latter does not correspond to the full value of $\tan \varphi$. Thus if the infilling material of the bedding planes or fissures is of clayey character, $\tan \varphi$ can decrease to about 65 %. Consequently, if rock bolts cooperate with the shear resistance of a rock mass, only 65 % of the classical shear strength should be considered. Under this condition the safety

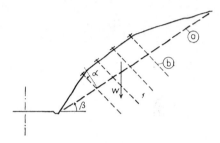

Fig. 8-15. Stabilization of the slope by prestressed rock-bolts; a — bedding plane, b — prestressed rock-bolt.

factor should exceed one. With a smaller factor of safety the slope yields and the stress in the rock bolts increases, until either the equilibrium is reached or the rock bolts yield, too. To avoid the yielding of the slope along a surface with clayey filling, it is necessary to prestress the rock bolts by such a force that the stability factor would be greater than one with the factor of shear resistance equal to $0.65 \tan \varphi$.

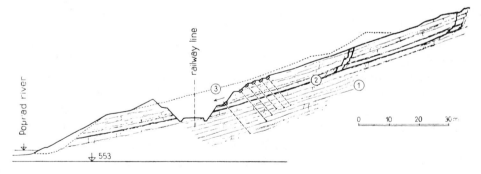

Fig. 8-16. Correction of the slide in the cutting on the railway line Podolinec-Orlov, Slovakia; 1 — Palaeogene sandstones and shales, 2 — bedding plane on which the movement took place, 3 — the original surface of the terrain.

155

The durability of rock bolts is a very delicate problem, as they can deteriorate in the environment of natural agents. Since the alloy steel does not resist corrosion the holes with rock bolts are to be grouted with bitumen, which is expensive

Fig. 8-17. Close-up view of the anchorage of the cutting slope shown in Fig. 8-16.

and cumbersome. Some progress has been achieved by the use of coating on the bolt surface, e.g. polyethylene coating, which cannot be damaged in mechanical ways. The hole is then grouted with cement mortar.

The factor of time is important during the installation of the rock bolts. Even with a very small movement of the slope the successively installed bolts can break and, therefore, it is necessary to install several bolts at once.

As an example, the anchoring of a rock slope in the approach cutting of a tunnel on the line Podolinec—Orlov may be mentioned. Beds of Palaeogene age, inclined to the valley, yielded after a partial excavation of the cutting and moved down very slowly. In the period of three years (from 1962 to 1965) the displacement amounted to 2—3 m. The dip of the beds is 21 degrees and as the rock is dry, it can be supposed that the angle of shear strength also equals 21 degrees.

As designed by Hobst, the slippage of beds is prevented by rock bolts (Vojen-

156

ské stavby, n. p., Brno, Technical Bulletin No. 3, 1965), Fig. 8-16. The anchorage consists of cables 60 mm in diameter, the ends of which were untangled and inserted into the boreholes (100 mm in diameter) which were enlarged by explosives at the end and grouted with cement mortar. The prestressing force of a cable is 100 Mp and the system of 238 anchors increases the stability factor from 1 to about 1.44. When considering the afore-said strength in relaxation the stability factor of just about one is obtained.

The anchoring in soils begins to develop in connection with the bracing of cuts. Pipes serve as drill rods and core bits are used as cutting heads. These serve as anchorage for a tie which is inserted into the drill pipes. After installing the tie the pipes are pulled out and the hole is grouted. The material of the ties should be resistant to corrosion.

8.7   Stabilization of slope by piles

The treatment of landslides by use of piles was employed on several occasions, mostly without success. With the exception of shallow landslides the forces mobilizing the slip movement are too great to be resisted by a row of

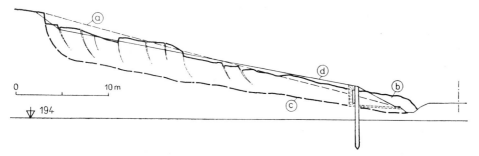

Fig. 8-18. Stabilization of the sheet slide by piles in a railway cutting (East Slovakia); a — graded slope of the cutting before the slide, b — slide from 1965, c — slip surface, d — regraded slope surface (from Nešvara).

piles. Shallow landslides can be controlled by piling because the piles can be driven to a depth satisfactory for adequate safety to be achieved. If the piles are not driven sufficiently deep, they tilt from the vertical position and, consequently, the consistency of the adjacent rock becomes disturbed, even beneath the slip surface, and the slide spreads out. Piling proves likewise ineffective if soft plastic soils move downslope because they may flow through the intervals between the piles. Piles may be used rather as a preventive measure since they appreciably increase the friction on potential slip surfaces.

In Czechoslovakia, piles were used as a corrective treatment of a landslide which occurred during the construction of the broad gauge railway at Nižná Myšla in eastern Slovakia. The line is laid in a cutting 8 metres in depth, excavated into the Neogene marly clay. The slope has the gradient of 1 in 4, since the material has the character of fissured clay and is predisposed to slaking and sliding. During the rainy spring in 1965 a small sheet slide developed at the toe of the slope, which extended to a length of 50 m and reached up to the top of the slope (Fig. 8-18). As the site of the slide was not accessible and a large removal of soil would be difficult, piles were employed to prevent the further spreading of the landslide. Forty-two piles, 6 m long, were driven into the prepared boreholes to a depth of 4 metres. Reinforced concrete slabs were supported against the piles to prevent movement of the soil between and around the piles. The pile spacing was 1 to 1.5 m. A sand drain was constructed along the slabs, discharging drained water to a ditch. After the treatment, the slope stabilized and was flattened to the gradient of 1 in 5.

8.8   Hardening of soils

In sect. 8.3 examples of the stabilization of slopes by means of surface drainage or subdrainage were cited This method fails with impermeable soils, where the zone affected by drainage is small. In this case methods adopted from foundation engineering and known as hardening of soils, may be considered.

The first of these methods, drainage by *electro-osmosis*, has the same final effect as the subdrainage, but differs in that water does not move toward the drainage by gravity, but by the activity of the electric field. If two electrodes are installed into a soil, the water contained in the soil migrates from anode towards the cathode. The cathode consists of a perforated pipe; water penetrates into it and can be removed by pumping. The method is best suited to the drainage of silty soils with particles between 0.05 and 0.005 mm. Clay particles contained in silt harden under the action of dewatering. The method fails with fine sand, since beginning with even a permeability of about 3 times 10^{-4} cm/sec the movement under the action of gravity overwhelms the effect of electric current. This holds true especially if for the sake of stability the ground water should be diverted from flowing towards the slope surface. The action of electro-osmosis can also be invalidated by the electrolytes in ground water which increase its conductivity and reduce its flow by electroosmotic forces. Under high voltage water can be resolved. Therefore, field tests are necessary to estimate the best parameters of energy supply and of effectiveness of drainage.

The idea of this method is old (Reuss, 1809), but its first practical application dates from the period of World War II. L. Casagrande (1941) employed it to stabilize the slopes of railway cuttings. Its best-known application of that period was in Norway during the occupation of the country by the German troops.

It was used for the construction of a tunnel and of a submarine base. At the latter site the excavation should have reached a depth of 14 m, the area being 230 by 160 m. The site was near the sea shore and the soil was built up of silt with an admixture of clay and interlayers of sand. In spite of protection by two rows of sheet pile walls 20 m deep, the bottom was heaved upwards by the influence of uplift when the excavation reached the depth of 8 m.

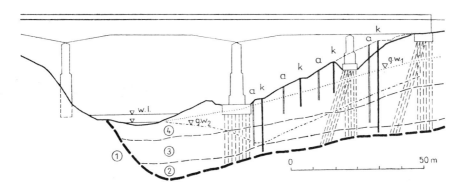

Fig. 8-19. Stabilization of a landslide by electro-osmosis (construction of a highway-bridge, Ontario in Canada); a — anode, k — cathode, 1 — bedrock, 2 — compact glaciofluvial sand with gravel, 3 — compact silt with sand seams, 4 — loosened silty sediments with sand seams. Intercalations of soft clay in silts caused the failure of slope. (g.w₁) — groundwater level before stabilization and (g.w₂) after the drainage by electroosmosis (Casagrande et al., 1961).

The upheaval made further excavation futile and the danger of slope failure arose. Hence, two rows of pipes were driven from the level of minus 8 metres. The diameter of tubes was 20 centimetres and the spacing (in both directions) was 10 m. They were installed alternately as anodes and cathodes and the voltage of the current was 40 volts. Prior to the action of the current the water yield from the cathodes was only 50 litres per hour each, and after it reached up to 479 litres. The total consumption of energy was 0.4 kWh for a day and for one cubic metre of the volume of the cutting.

An interesting recent example of the employment of electroosmosis for the stabilization was cited by Casagrande et al. (1961). During the driving of piles for the foundation of a bridge in Ontario, Canada, the slope of the valley collapsed. The valley is cut in glaciolacustrine deposits of silts with interbeds of sand and thin lenses of clay (Fig. 8-19). The slide filled in the excavation for the foundation of pier in the bottom of the valley and destroyed the template for driving the steel sheet piling. Laboratory and field tests indicated that the decrease of water content by electroosmosis from the average value of 26 % to about 23 % would produce the increase in strength sufficient to stabilize the slope.

159

Besides it was expected that the procedure would lower the water level in the permeable interbeds, but this effect was not considered in statical analysis. Based on the results of field tests, the procedure, consisting in treating the toe and the top sections of the slope to the full depth above the bedrock (21 and 36 m)

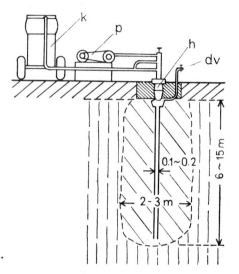 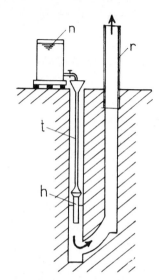

Fig. 8-20. Thermic treatment of loess according to Litvinov (1955); k — compressor, p — oil pump, h — mixing burner, dv — air inlet.

Fig. 8-21. Thermic treatment of clayey soil (Beles, 1957); n — tank with oil, t — oil intake pipe, h — mixing burner, r — chimney tube for draught producing.

and the remaining section to the depth of 12 m, was determined. Four rows of anodes and four rows of cathodes were installed. The spacing between the rows of anodes and cathodes varied from 3 to 10 m and the spacing along the rows was 1.8 m with the shallow electrodes and 3 m with the deep ones. The pumping pipes of the cathodes were installed in cased holes and furnished with filter. Under the action of the electric current with the voltage of 100—150 volts the water yield reached about 75 litres/min. After 3 months the water content in soil decreased about 4 % and the ground water level in the silty material dropped about 10 m near the top of the slope and about 13.5 m near the toe. The soil stabilized to such an extent that it was possible to excavate it with a slope gradient of 1 in 1, although the original slopes collapsed with the gradient of 1 in 2.5.

Exceptionally, the *thermic treatment* is employed for the stabilization of landslides. This method was discovered by Litvinov (1955; Novák, 1964) for the hardening of loess in the foundations of structures. A compressor (Fig. 8-20) drives air with the pressure of 0.15 to 0.5 atmospheres into a mixing burner, in which the oil conveyed from a special pump is burnt. The exhaustion gas with the temperature of about 1,000 °C is driven into the borehole and penetrates into the pores of the loess, which is baked into a hard material. The radius of activity is about 2 to 3 m. As far as we know, this method has not been employed for the stabilization of slopes, but it was used in a modified manner for the stabilization of landslides in clay by the Rumanian engineers (Beles and Stanculescu, in Beles, 1957). As clay contains no large pores as the loess

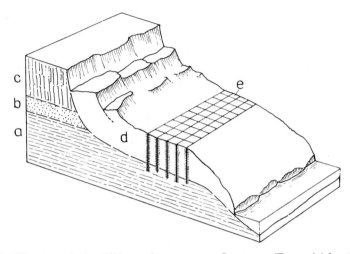

Fig. 8-22. Stabilization of a landslide on the coast near Constanza (Rumania) by thermic treatment (Beles, 1957); a — plastic clay, b — sand, c — loess-loam, d — slid mass, e — thermically treated part.

does, two holes are necessary (Fig. 8-21) which are connected to produce a draught. A chimney tube is set up at the exit, which is heated. Consequently, a considerable advantage of this method is in that no compressor is necessary. Oil is conducted by a pipe to a special burner installed in the borehole. It is ignited by a tissue which is laid on the upper cover of the burner and set on fire prior to inserting the burner into the borehole.

It this way, a shore slope near Constanza was treated by using several rows of boreholes (Fig. 8-22). Several cases of the stabilization of slopes in Czechoslovakia and critical comments on this method were cited by Novák (1964).

Of the other methods of the hardening of soils used in foundation engineering, the *grouting* with portland cement is worthy of mention. This method has been used successfully for hardening the railway subgrade and mud pockets underneath the roadbed. Nowadays it is also used for the stabilization of landslides on railways, as this method can be employed without disturbance of traffic.

In England, embankments and cuttings, even in clay, have been satisfactorily treated in this way. Experience shows that this method yields fine results with rather shallow landslides in stiff materials such as clay shales, claystones and stiff clays, which break into blocks separated by distinct fissures. On the other hand, slaked material cannot be grouted.

The effect of grouting consists in displacing water from the fissures, which are filled up with cement mortar. The latter hardens and creates a stable skeleton between the blocks. The method is in principle a mechanical stabilization of the slope and not a change in consistency of soil mass, as neither cement mortar nor a suspension can enter into the soil mass. The grouting begins with pressures larger than the weight of the overburden (4 to 6 atmospheres), which produce the penetration of the suspension along the fissures and along the active slip surface. At several sites a continuous layer of hardened cement mortar, 6 to 12 cm thick, originated along the slip surface and contributed considerably to the stabilization of the slope (Ayres, 1961).

Before using this method a clear picture of the depth and shape of the slip surface must be provided (Chapter 6). A row of boreholes is driven till underneath the slip plane and injection pipes are installed into the boreholes. Sometimes injection pipes can simply be rammed into the ground. After the experience gained in England, the grouting follows in rows parallel to the track and spaced 3—5 m. The grouting operation begins at the lowest row in order to create a fixed support near the toe of the endangered slope.

In Czechoslovakia the first application of this method took place in 1961 at the railway station Karlovy Vary (Brabec, 1962; Kraus and Kubíček, 1963). Tertiary tuffaceous clays cover the granite of Karlovy Vary, which is decomposed into kaolin at the surface. The depth of the slip plane was 3 to 8 m. The stabilization took place by boring nine rows of boreholes spaced 5 m. The rows of boreholes, 3 m apart, were directed perpendicularly to the track. The grouting liquid was aerated cement suspension and mortar (Aerocem). The casing, 5 cm in diameter, was driven manually and after achieving the specified depth, grouting pipes were inserted. Average consumption of cement mortar was 2.2 m³ for a borehole, the maximum consumption being up to 10.6 m³. The stabilization of about 8,000 m³ of landslides required 107 boreholes in a total length of 540 m and 88 tons of cement. The grouting pressure was 2 to 6 atmospheres. After the grouting procedure had finished, the movement stopped. But the lasting effect of this procedure depends on whether or not ground water will be stored by the grouted zone.

8.9   The break of the slip surface by blasting

On some occasions a break of the slip plane by blasting explosives was employed. The opinions on the use of this technique are controversial and mostly sceptical. No permanent effect is to be achieved with landslides in weak plastic soils.

This method is more promising with landslides along rather straight planes with hard rock underneath. When placing explosives into the hard rock one may expect that:

(a) The explosion will loosen the rock and uplift of the ground water will be reduced.

(b) The straight plane will be broken and the rock fragments will become mixed with the overlying clay material and increase its resistance in friction.

The effect is mostly temporary, as the fissures produced by explosion will gradually be filled up with clay particles and the volume of the sliding mass will increase by the amount of disturbed rock. The prevailing opinion is that this method is not to be employed for the control of deep landslides in fine-grained soils.

It appears that the main disadvantage of this method is in its unreliability. Its application is not possible at sites where the explosion may produce harm in the surrounding area. The measures concerning the quantity and the placing of explosives should be provided by an experienced expert.

Chapter 9

PREVENTION OF SLOPE FAILURES

The stabilization of landslides requires difficult and expensive treatment. Besides direct expenses, indirect ones should also be considered: the course of construction is jeopardized, additional equipment very often becomes necessary and losses caused by delay in the construction deadline occur. Landslides are of serious concern to the persons involved; the intensity of the natural phenomenon creates a depressive atmosphere and anxiety arises as to whether the collapsing slope can be stabilized at all. The question of guilt as to whether or not the failure could have been prevented, also arises. Experience shows that if the design can be altered so as to exclude the risk of a landslide even at the cost of a large increase in expenses, it is advisable for the designer to eschew the risk. The need of circumspect treatment of the troublesome slopes makes demands on the design as well as on the construction, which can be grouped as follows: refinement of the engineering-geological investigation (sect. 9.1), careful selection of the site (sect. 9.2), perfection of the design of earthworks (sect. 9.3] and a suitable technique of construction (sect. 9.4).

9.1   **Programme for engineering-geological exploration.** In spite of the fact that exploration methods have recently been improved, thanks to the progress in engineering geology and soil and rock mechanics, landslides still occur at many sites in the course of construction. Hence the refinement of exploration is necessary. There are, however, so many forms of landslides and so many factors contributing to their onset, that no satisfactory realistic instructions can be given as to the way the exploration should be improved and completed. In spite of this, some remarks on the actual state of exploration can be made, especially because several important factors are often neglected.

As stated in Chapter 5, the origin of landslides in many cases should be sought in the thin laminae along existing planes of discontinuity in rocks, such as the remoulded slip surfaces of old, even fossil, landslides, thin seams of sand containing water under pressure in cohesive soils, fault planes in rocks, etc. They are difficult to reveal by current techniques of exploration (Terzaghi, 1962; Záruba, 1962). This often results from an unsuitable boring technique as well as from the imperfect inspection of samples. Therefore, it seems that some methods of exploration should be revised along the following lines:

(a) Preference should be given to boring methods that ensure a sufficient sample recovery. This leads to the use of core drilling with a double-tube core barrel and to a dry boring, possibly with the addition of a small amount of water. Generally, short boring lengths are preferable, i. e. of only 0.4—0.6 m, and the premiums should be specified with respect to core recovery and to the effort to obtain it, and not with respect to the depth of the borehole. This should be applied especially for boring in some rocks of the Cretaceous or Tertiary age and in colluvial deposits.

(b) Methods of borings and sampling should yield information on the orientation of bedding planes and fissures and the nature of their fillings.

(c) In many cases a geologist should be permanently present at the site during boring. The pressure of ground water (pore water pressure in unconsolidated cohesive soils or uplift pressure in permeable interbeds of soil and rock masses) very often provokes the sliding of slopes. In many cases the routine methods of estimating ground water conditions are unsatisfactory. As a rule, several water horizons become interconnected by the borehole and in fine-grained soils the borehole itself affects the water regime in the surrounding ground. Thus it is necessary:

To install piezometers at the individual horizons and to observe the changes of the piezometer heads over a long period of time as well as in the course of construction.

To measure the vertical flow of water in boreholes connecting several horizons.

In Chapter 2 the detrimental effect of residual stress in soil and rock masses on the stability of slopes was demonstrated. Hence, the methods of its measurement should be refined and the results should be analyzed with respect to regional geology. The change of this stress in the course of construction should be studied.

Problems in the disintegration of aleuritic and pelitic hard sediments in the course of rebound should be studied by means of the methods of colloidal chemistry.

The strength of soils and rocks should be investigated in greater details than previously, and in a state and conditions which are as similar as possible to those in which they occur in the field.

9.2   Selection of the site

9.2.1   Structures of linear character (communications, sewers, canals). The designers frequently design linear constructions in the same manner in regions of a different geological character, considering only problems of gradients and curves, and the balancing of earthwork and an illusory reduction of costs. Thus, a road line is located in the same manner in the region of igneous rocks as in that of the Carpathian flysch, the only difference being in the gradient of slope, although in troublesome areas even small cuttings may provoke large landslides. The designers should respect the geological conditions of the area and the conception of the design should be thought out beforehand. For example, in the flysch regions it is preferable to locate the line in the flood plain or on the low terraces at the toe of the slopes, instead of laying it out into the slopes even with shallow cuttings. Several sections of the Púchov—Horní Lideč railway were located on fills in the flood plain in order to avoid numerous old landslides of the slopes (Fig. 5—9). The location of communications along reservoirs is very unfavourable in this respect, as the stability of slopes may also be threatened by the stored water. Therefore, it is often reasonable to divert the line outside the valley or to climb the slope high above the reservoir level, near to the peneplain.

9.2.2   **Urban planning.** In locating the dwelling and industrial buildings, the engineering-geological conditions of the site are often neglected. Intricate juridical interests may then arise, as by giving permission to build, the authorities have a certain liability towards the owner. In several countries an expert report by an engineering geologist is obligatory prior to the granting of building permission. The instability of slopes may also be provoked by the construction of streets, of service mains, cable lines, etc. In any case, urban plans should be inspected from the point of view of the stability of the area, and with respect to the changes connected with building activity. If the coverage of some troublesome areas is of great importance, their stabilization should be ensured long before construction begins.

The design of buildings in areas susceptible to sliding should, therefore, begin

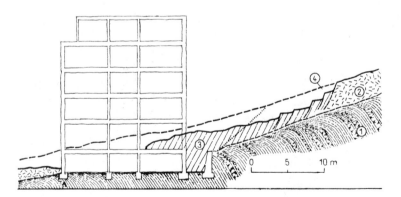

Fig. 9-1. Building damaged by sliding of slope debris, Luhačovice (Moravia); 1 — argillaceous shales and sandstones (Palaeogene), 2 — clayey-sandy slope debris, 3 — slid material, 4 — original slope surface.

166

with stabilization of slopes, in order to avoid their collapse, and hence, damage to the new structures. The construction of a sanatorium building in eastern Moravia can be presented as an example. The building is situated on a gentle slope of shales and sandstones of Palaeogene age (Fig. 9-1). The rock weathers readily and produces clayey-sandy detritus, which is prone to sliding. The slip plane generally originates on the surface of the bedrock, the bedding planes of which are usually bent downslope. In the given case the building was founded on the stable rock and the slope of the cutting was supported by a low retaining wall. The slope was excavated at a gradient of 1 in 1.5. After the reinforced concrete skeleton with facework had been erected, a sliding of detritus originated in the spring and the material filled the space between the retaining wall and the structure and broke through the facework of the ground-floor. However, the concrete structure was not damaged; the slaked material flowed onto the ground-floor around the columns. Repair was easily effected by removing the sliding mass and stabilizing the slope by several drainage trenches. It follows that the stabilization of the slope should precede the construction, on the basis of careful investigation.

9.2.3 **Hydrotechnic structures.** The problems connected with the hydrotechnic constructions involve (a) the selection of the dam site, (b) the design of the discharge canals, and (c) the stability of the shores of the future reservoir. If satisfactory care of them is not provided in the stage of design, large landslides and the considerable expenditure involved in their stabilization may result.

(a) When selecting a dam site, one should avoid those that exhibit sheer slopes with unstable rocks high above the dam crown. The stability of the slopes of a foundation pit is an important problem which influences the selection of the dam site. The construction of the foundations usually requires deep excavation. In general, sites without steep slopes reaching up high above the dam crown are less dangerous. In many cases expensive measures were necessary to stabilize the slope in the course of foundation excavation and several times it was necessary to abandon the site.

(b) Another problem of great importance is the location of discharge canals with respect to the stability of slopes. If the slopes are hazardous it is better to lay out the canal in the flood plain even though two dikes have to be constructed. The problem of the design of the canal near Turany on the river Váh (Fig. 9-2) can be quoted. The first alternative proposed the laying-out of the canal in a cutting, which touched the areas of old landslides. Loss of their stability could be expected; in addition, the clayey-sandy detritus was not suitable for the construction of embankments. This led to alternative II: The canal was located in the flood plain in spite of the necessity of constructing two dikes and of their difficult foundation. The difficulties arose because an old channel of the Váh had been eroded into the bedrock of the flood plain and later on filled with compressible peat material. Partial removal of this material was necessary to avoid differential settlement of the canal body which could damage its lining.

(c) Stability of the shores of a reservoir. When designing dams the stability of the valley slopes should be analyzed, especially with respect to the fluctuation of the water level. Two factors provoking collapse must be considered:

The stability of rock and soil masses changes when they become submerged. The uplift reduces the effective unit weight, while the weight above water level

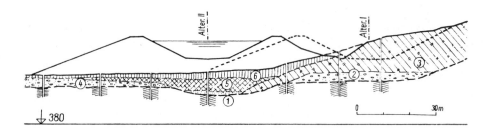

Fig. 9-2. The influence of geological conditions on the design of discharge canal. Alternative solution I would cause the disturbance of slope stability; alternative II required the removal of strongly compressible peat; 1 — marly shales, 2 — terrace sandy gravels, 3 — clayey-sandy debris redeposited by sliding, 4 — sandy gravels of the Váh valley-plain, 5 — peat deposits, 6 — sandy loams.

remains unchanged. Moreover, the cohesion of fine-grained soils decreases. The rapid draw-down increases the tangential components of the weight and the seepage produces large forces on the mass.

Wave motion produced by wind erodes the shores analogically to the activity of waves along the sea coasts. A typical wave-cut terrace or platform, limited by the cliff, originates. A wave-built terrace is formed in the shore deposits. The fluctuation of the water level in reservoirs is larger than in natural lakes. The water level changes regularly during the day and in the course of the year. Hence, erosion of shore deposits occurs and the material is transported down the slopes toward the bottom. The slope is undercut by the cliff and can slip down.

As long as stable bedrock appears in the cliff, the sliding of slope is only exceptional, being limited to the occurrence of inclined bedding planes or fissures. Sometimes large stabilization works are necessary. The treatment of the left slope of the reservoir of the Pontesei dam in the area of the river Piave in Italy can be cited (Capra and Linari, 1960; Walters, 1962). Triassic limestone beds cropped out on the sheer slope inclined at 30° toward the valley. Fissures in the upper section of the slope indicated the danger of collapse, which was increased by the construction of a road tunnel. Therefore, the toe of the slope

168

was supported against the opposite slope by a large reinforced concrete structure (Fig. 9-3).

If the slope is covered with detritus, loam, terrace deposits or other young surface materials, the problem of the stability of shores deserves great attention.

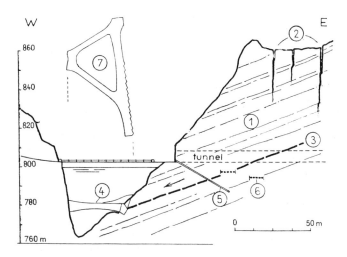

Fig. 9-3. Preventive measures against sliding of Triassic limestones into the Pontesei reservoir; 1 — Triassic limestones, 2 — gaping fissures, 3 — presumed slip surface, 4 — reinforced concrete structure, 5 — inspection boring, 6 — measurement device (on bedding planes outside the section), 7 — ground-plan of reinforced-concrete structure (Capra and Linari, 1960).

If the slope cover is thick and especially if slope movements have occurred in the past, the fluctuation of the water level in the reservoir can produce landslides, which extend high above the level of the stored water.

Such accidents have occurred, for example, in the Appennines, where the problem of slopes sliding into reservoirs is one of the most important factors in preliminary geological investigation (Segré, 1924). In the zone of Carpathian flysch, too, many areas exist, where after filling the reservoirs the movement of slopes is reactivated. For instance, after storage of the reservoir near Roźnów on the river Dunajec in Poland the shores, consisting of weathered flysch rocks, were badly damaged. Landslide movements extended high above the water level so that several roads were damaged.

The slopes of the future reservoir should be carefully examined, irrespective of the composition of rocks. When comparing several designs with different levels of impounded water, the decision may be influenced by the difference in costs necessary for the stabilization of slopes, especially when valuable grounds or building sites could be endangered.

169

9.3   The design of earthworks

The design of excavations and fills in areas susceptible to sliding should follow the rule that the toe of the slope should remain weighted as far as possible. This follows from two phenomena discussed in Chapter 2: Firstly, after the removal of the weight of the overburden the shear strength of rocks and soils decreases. Secondly, the decrease in residual horizontal stress after excavation produces a loosening of the slopes.

Consequently, when designing the shape of a slope in pelitic rocks or soils, it is necessary to keep in mind that the unloaded material at the toe slackens, which contributes to the deterioration caused by the seepage of ground water. Therefore simple flattening of a slope often does not prevent landslides. Several cases could be quoted, where the slope angle was changed several times during the excavation, each time with expensive grading and lining of the surface, and still the movement of the slope was repeated. It is also due to the fact that the width of the flattened slope increases and the quantity of rain water soaked into the ground grows, while the drainage conditions become impeded.

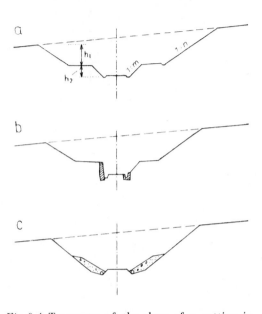

Fig. 9-4. Treatment of the slope of a cutting in clayey rocks; a — stooped slope, b — lower part of the slope protected by retaining wall, c — the toe of slope surcharged by gravel bench.

Therefore, a design should aim at the reduction of the width of the slope near the bottom. Several modifications of this principle come into consideration:

(a) A stooped slope (Fig. 9-4). The slope is divided into two sections separated by a bench. The upper one is generally larger and its angle is chosen with respect to the seepage of rain water. The angle of the lower section is as large as possible with respect to h_2. Therefore h_2 is designed relatively small, about 6 m with cuttings up to a depth of 20 m and the drainage of the mass underneath the bench, e.g. by means of horizontal boreholes, is very beneficial. The width of the bench is given by the stability analysis of the slope as a whole. In this way the influence of decreased strength due to removal of material near the bottom is reduced. Rain water collected from the upper section of the slope

170

is generally conducted to the bottom of the cut by impermeable ditches at the berm and by gutters.

(b) The step-like shape of slopes is often emphasized by erecting higher or lower retaining walls (Fig. 9-4b), which contribute to the reduction of the removal of material at the bottom of the cut. Moreover, there are other advantages: the toe of the slope, where the freezing of ground water may lead to the development of slumps, is protected. The cleaning of bottom ditches becomes easier, etc. On the other hand, the construction is complicated, as the need of skilled labour increases.

This shape of cuts has long been the practice in the areas of Neogene in Moravia. The more than hundred-years-old railway cuttings in clay and marl on the Brno—Přerov and Přerov—Bohumín lines offer an example. This shape of a cutting often had other advantages. Loess and loess-loam excavated in the upper portion of a cutting were suitable for the construction of embankments, whereas the clay material of the reduced lower portion was used for the counter dams at the bottom of embankments. The differentiation of the materials also led to a gradual excavation of the cuttings which improved their stability.

(c) The demands on the mechanization of excavation works are not in keeping with the shape of slope as mentioned in the preceding point. These requirements are better fulfilled by the shape shown in Fig. 9-4c, where the bench is constructed of gravel. Not only can machine labour be used, but also the gravel fill shelters the toe of the slope from frost and drains water from the slope. The longitudinal water collectors can also be protected by the fill. The width of the gravel bench should be found by stability analysis, but in every case it should be large enough for the transport of gravel. Instead of gravel benches, other structures with a similar statical function can be employed, such as rubblework, filled crib walls, etc. (sect. 8.5).

9.4   Construction operations

The mechanization of excavation implies great progress as compared with manual work, but on the other hand, it contributes to a greater frequency of slides on the slopes of cuttings. While methods of exploration have been refined, construction operations have become unpropitious for the stability of cuts. Therefore, the stability of slopes must be respected in the course of excavation work. In dangerous soils the following instructions should be followed:

Firstly, excavation in layers is advisable, so as to avoid the formation of high working faces. This has two advantages; one giving the possibility of progressive drainage of the cut, the other concerning the origin of tensile zones.

In the course of excavation in sections, the ground water level is progressively lowered and the stability of slopes increases. Consequently, today too, this procedure should be applied in excavating. The custom of concentrating excavators at one site instead of distributing them in several cuts is detrimental to the stability of slopes. Large cuttings should not be left as one of the terminal steps in the construction of communications, but it should proceed gradually with other works. If excavation is to be finished within a short time, at least the drainage of the site should be ensured beforehand. The installation of horizontal boreholes is often possible prior to excavation.

Cuttings with high vertical faces are hazardous from the point of view of stability. The upper layers of rocks and soils neighbouring the excavation are subjected to tensile strains. The area under tension is not limited by the boundaries of the future cutting, especially when horizontal residual stress occurs. The notion that a landslide caused by exposing high sheer face has the same extent as that which would appear with excavation in layers, is incorrect.

Another factor, neglected in the course of earthworks, is the drainage of cuttings and of adjacent grounds. With mass excavations the ways in which water penetrates into the cut are not realized. Agricultural drainage pipes may be cut by excavation and water escapes from them into the slope. In such case the drainage collectors should be drained with pipes or gutters at some distance from the edge of the cutting. Stripped topsoil is often deposited along the cutting crown, without considering that rain water can be stored and penetrate into the ground. This, together with the weight of the heaps, may cause landslides.

The construction of drainage trenches in the slopes is often stereotyped. They are located according to the design without considering the actual conditions. Cases could be quoted where the drainage trenches were constructed in dry portions of the slope, whereas water appearing in the neighbourhood remained unnoticed. Drainage trenches are installed after the excavation is accomplished, and thus landslides originate long before. Today, when several methods of driving horizontal boreholes have been developed, slopes could be drained not only more effectively, but also earlier.

Often the drainage of the bottom of excavations is also neglected. A shallow drainage trench should be excavated in the bottom of each layer. Often drainage sumps are necessary and water is diverted by pumping. In very unsatisfactory conditions drainage by pumping from wells is necessary as a provisory arrangement, which is replaced by horizontal drainage boreholes after the excavation is accomplished.

Water conducted from the cutting should not escape observation. Often it can produce landslides of the lower sections of the slope, which can endanger not only other structures but also the construction itself.

An excessive consumption of explosives can disintegrate rock mass and provoke sliding movements. Water can penetrate into the loosened mass and infringe on its strength.

172

Very often retaining walls have to be constructed in sections in shafts. The space between the back of the wall and the rock should be filled without delay. A drainage is necessary underneath the base of the wall and water should be pumped out from the shafts. Foundation excavations situated on slopes should be drained by means of horizontal boreholes driven prior to the construction.

Chapter 10

SURVEY OF LANDSLIDES ON THE TERRITORY OF CZECHOSLOVAKIA

The systematic investigation and registration of landslides carried out during 1962—1963 provided quite a satisfactory review of the distribution of landslides on Czechoslovak territory. The action was called forth by the disastrous landslide near Handlová in 1961. On the basis of field research a generalized map of slide areas on a scale of 1 : 200,000 was compiled. The results of this action, in which more than twenty engineering geologists took part, have been summed up in the conclusive report "Investigation of slide areas of Czechoslovakia", compiled by the editorial board consisting of M. Matula, A. Nemčok, J. Pašek, L. Řepka and M. Špůrek (1963). At the same time a synoptic stability map and a map of landslide frequency (1 : 1,000,000) was prepared. A simplified and partly modified map on a scale of 1 : 2,500,000 is attached to the present work. All data on the landslide registration are deposited in the archives of the Geological Survey (Geofond).

In some regions of Czechoslovakia slope movements are very frequent and their origin is due mainly to the lithology of the rocks and to topographical conditions. Fresh movements are invariably motivated by extraordinarily high rainfall. Landslides affect predominantly Quaternary sediments and imperfectly consolidated pelitic Tertiary and Cretaceous formations. With the exception of Permo-Carboniferous, sliding phenomena in older geological formations are comparatively rare under the present climatic conditions.

Slope movements of the most varied forms occurred to a much larger degree during the Pleistocene, being caused by abrupt climatic changes. Apart from annual climatic cycles, long-termed oscillations were recurrent during the glacial and interglacial stages. It was especially the periglacial climate that led to extensive slope movements, to solifluction and large landslides.

As during the Pleistocene, large masses of particularly soft rocks were removed by denudation both in the Bohemian Massif and the Carpathians, the remains of ancient landslides are found only occasionally, when buried by the youngest loess cover or slope deposits. They are revealed by detailed boring research or extensive earthworks.

10.1   Development and distribution of landslides in the Bohemian Massif

In the Bohemian Massif, landslides are connected mainly with formations built up partly of poorly consolidated rocks. They are most abundant in the Upper Cretaceous of Bohemia, in the volcanic rocks of the České Středohoří Mts. emplaced on the Cretaceous, in the Tertiary brown-coal basins of northern

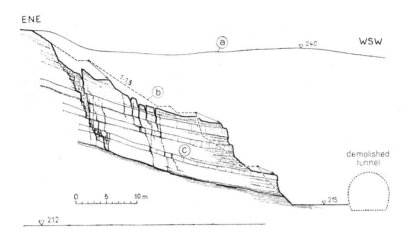

Fig. 10-1. Landslide of the cutting at Bohdalec in Prague; a — original surface of the terrain, b — graded slope of the excavation, c — slip of shales along bedding planes.

Bohemia and in the Tertiary marine rocks in the area of Ústí nad Orlicí (eastern Bohemia); their frequency in some Permo-Carboniferous regions is quite appreciable.

In older formations landslides are comparatively scarce, but some deep valleys may provide favourable conditions for their development. Thus, for instance, folded Ordovician complexes of shales and quartzites on the area of the city of Prague tend to slip down along the bedding planes where the slope is steeper than the dip of beds. The stability of these complexes may be disturbed by river erosion, or artificially induced by undermining the foot of the slope.

The susceptibility to sliding is particularly pronounced in the complexes of Králův Dvůr Shales and Kosov Quartzites. Excavating work often triggers the slide of large blocks, because the shales are very fine-grained and bedding planes as well as fragments are often lined with a clay film.

In the Prague area, the slide near Radotín (Myslil and Šilar, 1953) and several slope movements in foundation pits and railway cuttings took place in the Králův Dvůr Shales. Fig. 10-1 shows a cutting through the Bohdalec elevation at Nusle, excavated for the enlargement of a railway track, which should replace an old one-track tunnel. The slope is formed of the Králův Dvůr Shales with quartzite

175

Fig. 10-2. A complex of shales and quartzites loosened by sliding, slope of the Bohdalec cutting in Prague (photograph by Záruba).

intercalations. The beds are openly folded and in the south-eastern part are inclined at $15-20°$ into the cutting. The rocks were set into motion already during excavation; the slope was graded at 1 : 1 in the lower part and at 1 : 1.5 in the upper part, with three horizontal benches. During winter, a sheet of about 8,000 m³ in volume slipped into the cutting from the upper part of the slope which sank $2-3$ m along a steep fissure. The slide was limited to that part of the slope where shales formed a slight synclinal bend. The rock moved as a uniform complex but the part loosened by the movement was traversed by numerous, roughly vertical fissures; in particular, the firm quartzite beds were cut transversely into small cubes separated by open cracks (Fig. 10-2). In view of the gentle dip of the beds and the relatively great strength of the rocks with no inflow of water, the movement was unexpected and rather difficult to explain statically. As the cutting was 25 m deep, a certain amount of horizontal residual stress in the shales could not be excluded, which, being released by the excavation, produced the slip of beds.

In the Permo-Carboniferous, landslides particularly affect the weathering residues of Permian clayey-sandy argillites (shaly claystones). In the deep-cut valleys of the Džbán plateau (near Rakovník), built up of Permian argillites

Fig. 10-3. The frontal part of a landslide in Senonian marls near Mladá Boleslav (Bohemia)
(photograph by Záruba).

and overlying Cenomanian sandstones, slope movements are numerous. Marginal
sandstone blocks separated by vertical joints sank progressively into the soft
Permian substratum and moved downslope concurrently. They date mostly
from the Pleistocene and are topographically marked up to the present. In
places, as, for instance, in the valley near Pochvalov, movements were repeated
not very long ago. The liability of Permian rocks to slipping led to a number
of slides on the slopes of the railway cuttings during the construction of the
Rakovník—Louny line. Movements continued also after construction had been
completed and the corrective treatment of slopes on a large scale was necessary
(Fischer, 1930). In the Permo-Carboniferous of the Krkonoše foothills major
landslides developed between Semily and Jilemnice in the Jizera river valley,
and near Hostinné in the valley of the Labe river. Slope movements on the
basalt hill near Podbořany show a somewhat different character: marginal
blocks of a basalt flow move down-slope together with basalt debris and the
underlying Permo-Carboniferous clay.

10.1.1 **Landslides in the Cretaceous formations of Bohemia.** In this region landslides are abundant wherever Cretaceous rocks have pelitic character. On the

177

gentle slopes where Upper Turonian or Senonian marls crop out, sheet landslides are widespread. They originate at the sites of ground-water issues from sandy beds, or at spring thaw after a long freezing period during which near-surface beds have been enriched by water rising from the unfrozen substratum. The movement of shallow sheet slides is occasionally reactivated by heavy downpours following

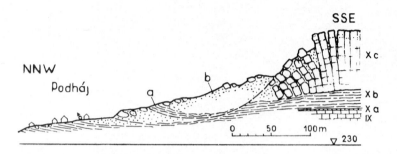

Fig. 10-4. Section of ancient Podháj landslide at the margin of the Cretaceous Plateau near Turnov (Bohemia); IX — Upper Turonian sandy marls, Xa — glauconitic sandstone, Xb — clayey marls, Xc — Lower Senonian thick-bedded sandstone, a — drawn-out marls along slip surface, b — sandy slope debris (Záruba, 1952).

after a long dry spell. Rainwater penetrates to a depth of 1.5—2.5 m through a system of vertical cracks resulting from the shrinking of marls.

Examples of this landslide type occur near Mladá Boleslav and around Mělník wherever marlstones, fresh or weathered, are directly exposed to atmospheric agencies.

Occasionally, though not very often, sheet slides develop into earth flows; lubricated marlstones accumulate in a furrow or brook channel, to move down-slope as a continuous flow. This was the case observed in the Jičín area and on the slope of the Chlomek ridge, and elsewhere (Fig. 10-3).

Landslides of a different type originated in places where marlstones are over-lain by sandstones. Sandstone beds are mostly subhorizontal and vertically jointed which imposes on them a prismatic jointing. They constitute well-known "Rock-cities" with relatively high sheer rock walls. Marginal sandstone blocks sink progressively into soft underlying marlstones, squeezing them out. Such block landslides are mostly of Pleistocene age and formed under periglacial climatic conditions. As far as the above-mentioned phenomena have been studied, no signs indicating the sinking of marginal blocks have been observed in the pre-sent climate. The present-day humid climate is responsible for a very intensive surface weathering of sandstones manifested by the disintegration of blocks and the accumulation of voluminous sandy debris at the foot of the walls.

The growing debris cover, especially when soaked by water after heavy rainfall, contributes largely to the loading of the underlying marlstones. Their

178

shear resistance being decreased, landslides originate at the foot of sandstone walls along deep-lying curved slide surfaces. The slide at the foot of Mužský Hill near Mnichovo Hradiště from 1926 (Fig. 1-3) and the Postglacial landslide near Podháj in the Turnov area (Fig. 10-4) are of this type. Pleistocene block slides have been noticed at the margins of the Cretaceous Table, e.g. in the Motol

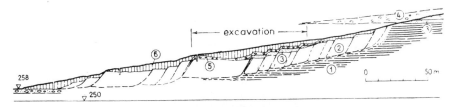

Fig. 10-5. Pleistocene block slides on the northern Stebénka slope near Turnov; 1 — Upper Turonian sandy marls, 2 — slid blocks of marl, 3 — green glauconitic sandstones, 4 — Pleistocene terrace gravels in original position, 5 — drawn-out terrace gravels, 6 — loess loam (Záruba, 1961).

valley near Prague (Fig. 5-32), in the Stebénka valley at Turnov (Záruba 1961). Loess sheets and fossil soils covering these block slides point to the Pleistocene age of the latter (Fig. 10-5).

10.1.2 **Landslides in the České středohoří Mts.** In the České středohoří Mts., Cretaceous complexes are represented by Upper Turonian to Senonian marlstones on the surface of which remnants of Tertiary volcanics, basalt flows with tuff and agglomerate interbeds, have been preserved. Volcanic rocks build up

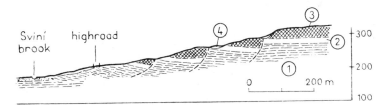

Fig. 10-6. Diagrammatic section of a block slide, near Bystřany in northern Bohemia; 1 — Lower Senonian marls, 2 — basalt tuff, 3 — basalt sheet, 4 — loess (Fencl and Záruba, 1956).

steep-sided elevations and table-mounts with sheer walls. Marginal blocks separated by vertical fissures sink again into soft Cretaceous marly substratum.

A major slide of this type was revealed during detailed mapping carried out for the building plan of the town of Teplice (Fencl and Záruba, 1956). The prominence between Drahkov and Bystřany is capped by a basalt sheet about 40 m thick lying on tuffs and marls of Cretaceous age. At the margin of the slope there is a head scarp roughly 600 m long, below which the sheet is broken into

179

several blocks moved valleywards (Fig. 10-6). The steps between sunken basalt blocks are partly levelled out by loess sheets which suggests the Pleistocene date for these slope movements. The slide planes probably do not extend deep

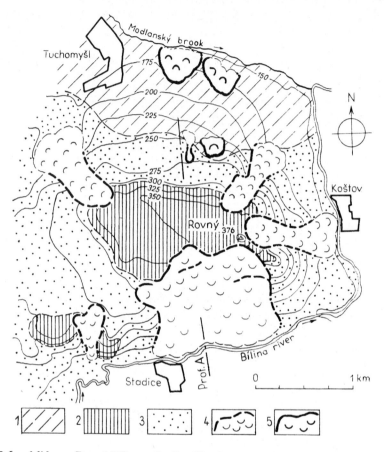

Fig. 10-7. Landslides on Rovný Hill near Stadice (North Bohemia); 1 — Neogene clay, 2 — basalt sheet, 3 — tuffs and tuffites, 4 — fossil landslides, 5 — recent landslides (after Kleček).

into the marls; it seems that plastic deformations of the surface layer of lubricated marls are involved in this case. Towards the end of the Last Glacial, the thawing of deep frozen marls (perenially frozen ground) furnished favourable conditions for their origin.

Analogous slope movements have been ascertained in a basalt quarry near Obrnice (Záruba and Mencl, 1954) and in many other localities in the České středohoří Mts.

Thus, for instance, in the Bílina river valley the slopes of Rovný Hill, N of Stadice, are scarred by landslides of various age and size (Fig. 10-7). The largest occurs on the southern slope where tuffs, clays and diatomaceous clays are capped by a basalt sheet, approximately 70 m thick. Several basalt blocks are shifted downslope; one of them, up to 200 m long, is tilted 18° upslope and constitutes a conspicuous edge. The head scarp is almost 1.4 km long and buried by bouldery basalt scree. Slide movements were initiated in the Pleistocene but fresh deformations and cracks observable on the surface of the boulder field indicate that the slope is not yet at rest.

Landslides below the Hazmburk Castle caused great damage in the Klapý community. The hill is made up of nepheline basanite with dense columnar jointing; voluminous scree accumulates in the upper part of the slope loading

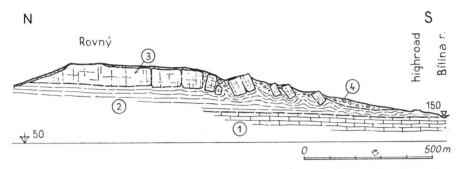

Fig. 10-8. Section of fossil block slide (prof. A in Fig. 10-7) on the Rovný slope; 1 — Upper Turonian sandy marls, 2 — tuffs and tuffites, 3 — basalt sheet, 4 — bouldery debris (after Kleček).

the underlying Cretaceous marls. On several occasions heavy rainfall was a motivating factor for extensive landslides (i.e. 1882, 1900 and 1939) with disastrous results (Počta, 1915; Woldřich, 1899; Stejskal, 1939).

Numerous traces of landslides may be found on the steep slopes of the Labe river valley within the České středohoří Mts. The largest slide seems to have occurred on the left riverside near Velké Březno. On January 5th and 6th in 1770, Cretaceous marls and trachyte debris slipped down and, according to contemporaneous records, partly blocked the Labe channel (Hibsch, 1903). Another large rockfall referred to (Hibsch, 1904) took place on the left bank of the Labe river, S of Vrkoč Hill, where basalt blocks rolled down on the present Labe floodplain and into the river bed.

In the Doupovské hory Mts. volcanic rocks and their debris often slip on the surface of clayey tuffs. In this area landslides are not so frequent but are larger; near Stružná on the southern periphery of the Doupovské hory an earthflow attains a length of 3 km and a volume of more than 10 million m³. The masses forming the toe of the landslide are accumulated on the granite basement.

The frequency of landslides in the České středohoří and the Doupovské hory areas is caused by the lithological character of the rocks and, consequently, the

181

topographical conditions. The prominences are capped by volcanic rocks, predominantly basalts and their agglomerates resistant to weathering. The slopes
are made up of relatively soft clayey tuffs or Cretaceous marls. As the upper
edges of the elevations are protected by firm rocks, the slopes developed such
steep gradients that they cannot permanently retain a stable position.

The concave banks of the deep Ohře river valley are disturbed by slumps
developed along curved, roughly cylindrical slide surfaces. The section of the
landslide at Březno near Postoloprty (Fig. 10-9) may serve as an illustration.

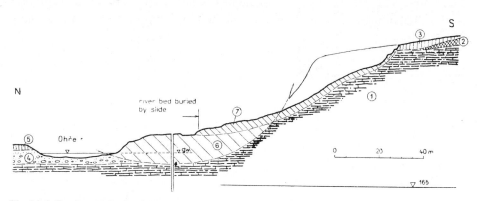

Fig. 10-9. Section of the landslide at Březno near Postoloprty (modified after Pašek); 1 — sandy
marls (Upper Turonian); 2 — baked Neogene clays, 3 — loess loam, 4 — sandy gravels, 5 — alluvial loam, 6 — old slide-mass (marls), 7 — younger slide-mass.

The slump is situated on the northern slope of the elevation towering above the
flat relief owing to a hard layer of baked claystones on the top, which protected
the Cretaceous marls from denudation. Lateral erosion of the meandering river
carved an almost 40 m high steep slope and finally disturbed its stability
(the shear resistance of marls was surpassed). Marls slipped down along a cylindrical slide surface and at the foot of the slope a large block of Cretaceous marlstones was squeezed out into the river. They are clearly seen on the river bottom,
as beds dipping at $10-15°$ into the slope; this inclination indicates the course
of the slide surface, because outside the landslide the Cretaceous beds lie almost
horizontally.

During spring thaw the root area is disturbed in many places by surface
slides. The surface marl bed of mushy consistence flows towards the foot of the
slope. The accumulated lubricated marls increase the load of the active part
of the landslide which moves periodically streamwards. The temporary stability
is also disturbed by lateral erosion of the river which carries away the frontal
portion of the bulge. From the shape of the meander it can be inferred that the
landslide partly blocked the ancient Ohře channel, shifting it about 40 m towards
the north.

182

Fig. 10-10. Cretaceous marls which have slipped down near Březno partly block the channel
of the Ohře river (photograph by Záruba).

In this reach of the Ohře river there is a series of similar but smaller slumps.
Their kettle-shaped scars are clearly seen on the banks. The bulges of slipped
mass, however, are not preserved; the material was carried away by floods.

10.1.3   Landslides in the Tertiary North Bohemian Basins.

Numerous landslides
also occur in the pelitic rocks of the North-Bohemian Brown-coal Basin. The
steep concave banks of the Ohře river and major brooks furnish favourable
conditions for their origin. Thus, for instance, the valley slopes of the Chomutov
brook between Chomutov and Postoloprty or of the Ostrava brook near Žatec
are scarred by large landslides of various age.

Geological research for the Nechranice earth dam on the Ohře river revealed
deep-reaching slumps in the Neogene clays at two levels. The base of the upper
ones, which are only partly preserved, lies approximately at the level of the
Middle Pleistocene terrace (about 20 m above the Ohře level), the lower ones are
confined to the present valley plain. The surface of the slope is partly levelled
by solifluction and slope deposits.

The proneness to sliding and scars of ancient slides are perceptible on the
slopes of abandoned meanders developed by the Ohře river during the Pleistocene.
Landslides originated particularly in places where springs flow from river
terraces or sand interbeds in Tertiary complexes. On the periphery of Žatec,
these slides are a serious obstacle to the growth of the town and some of them
even endanger ancient, medieval buildings.

Landslides of large size in the brown-coal basins are caused by human activity
and affect the slopes of opencast mines and of waste-dumps. Although deep pits
are excavated in several benches, steep slopes are often subject to sliding, chiefly

at the site of former mine workings. As long as the slides are confined to individual benches they can be corrected without great difficulty during the progress of work; corrective treatment however, is not so easy when a slump has disturbed all partial working levels of the quarry face (Fig. 10-11).

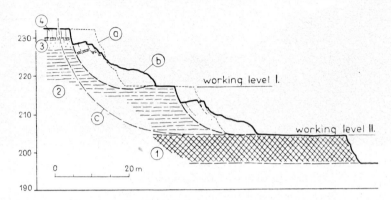

Fig. 10-11. Scheme of landslides promoted on the slopes of brown-coal opencasts by stripping the overburden; 1 — coal seam, 2 — overlying clays, 3 — sands, 4 — loess loam, a — steep slope due to excavation by wheel excavator, b — partial slides of benches; slide along main surface (c) endangers the whole slope.

In the North Bohemian Brown-coal Basin the deposition of overburden poses a serious problem. Old exhausted open pits which would be the most convenient for this purpose, are scarce so that the stripped material must be deposited in tip-heaps. Because of their great heights, the stability of the substratum is often

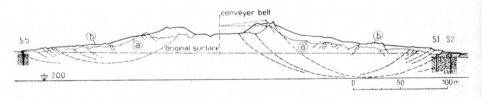

Fig. 10-12. Clay overburden piled into temporary waste-dumps produced squeezing-out of incompetent substratum and sliding of dump slopes near Most in northern Bohemia; a — state in May 1948, b — state in August 1948.

disturbed and beds of a low-bearing strength are squeezed out. Fig. 10-12 shows the surveyed section through one of the temporary tip-heaps near Most whose weight caused the underlying Tertiary clays to spread to all sides.

Isolated denudation remnants of Tertiary rocks occur at several places along the Boskovice Furrow, extending as far as Ústí nad Orlicí. They are made up of marls and silts laid in a bay of the Neogene sea ingressing from the Carpathian

184

Foredeep. Slide areas confined to these pelitic sediments are situated round Ústí nad Orlicí and Česká Třebová; there, the frequency of landslides is caused not only by lithology and topography but also by high rainfall.

10.2   Distribution and types of landslides in the Carpathian area

In eastern Moravia and Slovakia, the regions belonging to the Carpathian system, slope movements are more frequent than in the Bohemian Massif and are provoked mainly by topographical conditions. The Carpathian mountain ranges, being much younger than the Bohemian Massif, have not been levelled to such a degree by denudation and their relief is far more dissected. Watercourses cut their valley deep in to the bedrock and developed steep slopes liable to sliding. In the Carpathians, landslides occur particularly in the following areas:

(1) Flysch Belt.
(2) Margins of Tertiary volcanic complexes.
(3) Neogene of the Carpathian Foredeep.
(4) Palaeogene and Neogene of the Intra-Carpathian depressions.
(5) Landslides are comparatively rare in the Mesozoic of the Core-mountains and rockfalls occur sporadically on the slopes of mountains and valleys overdeepened by Pleistocene glaciers.

10.2.1   **Landslides in the Carpathian flysch area.** Flysch complexes are characterized by the alternation of shaly claystones and marlstones with sandstone beds. The wide distribution of landslides in flysch regions is conditioned by the easy weathering of bedrock, mainly of shaly claystones. Climatic agents, especially frost action, produce rapid disintegration of the claystones into thin flaky fragments, which soften in the presence of water and change gradually into clayey-sandy soils of adverse physical properties. They are unstable in volume, swelling and slaking when wet and shrinking strongly in a prolonged drought. Flysch complexes weather readily and are most liable to sliding mainly when thin sandstones and claystones alternate in finely rhythmical development.

The erosion activity of streams leads mostly to the development of large sheet slides, which under suitable topographical conditions pass into earthflows (sect 5.1.3).

In the periglacial conditions during the Pleistocene, slide movements attained their maximum extent, as evidenced by ancient slide surfaces and other traces of fossil landslides in the slope deposits. On some slopes, several generations of slides have been noted. They are usually separated by an erosive phase documented by alluvial cones, as recorded, for instance, by Andrusov from the Orava valley (1931).

The most notable flysch slide areas lie in the Vlára Pass, the Lysá Pass, and in the valleys of the rivers Dřevnice, Ostravice, Kysuca, Orava, Poprad and Ondava. The nature and the areal extent of flysch landslides in the Orava valley are shown on the map in Fig. 10-13.

Where the mountain slopes are built up of coarse-rhythmical flysch, thick beds of sandstone alternate with pelitic and aleuritic rocks. Sandstones, being

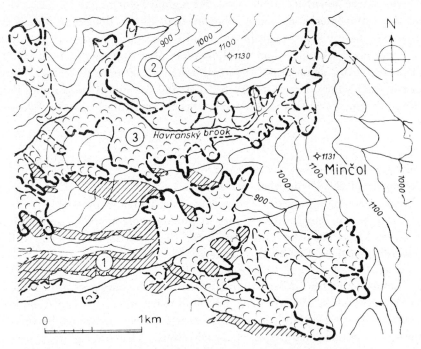

Fig. 10-13. Mountainous slopes affected by sliding occupy large areas in the Orava region, Slovakia; 1 — limestones of the Klippen Belt, 2 — Palaeogene argillaceous shales and sandstones in the flysch facies, 3 — landslides (from Andrusov).

weather-resistant, usually make up the summit parts of the ridges; in places, they are disrupted by slope movements into isolated blocks separated by wide gullies. Novosad (1966) described a similar case in the Beskydy Mountains. On the summit of Lukšinec Hill, a more than 70 m thick complex of Godula Sandstone lies on the inclined Lower Godula beds, which display a fine rhythmical development and a prevalence of claystones. The change in the composition of rocks is manifested by the issues of ground water at the surface of the claystones (Fig. 10-14). In the upper part of the slope, sandstone blocks slipped in the direction of the maximum tilt of the underlying claystones and a partial sinking of marginal blocks took place. Similar slope movements have also been observed on the slopes of Mount Radhošť, etc. The loosening of the

Godula Sandstone of the left abutment of the Morávka dam site is presumably an analogous phenomenon at an initial stage.

Soft rocks of the flysch complexes are also responsible for the sliding of some travertine elevations which overlie them. Ancient travertine mounds are traversed

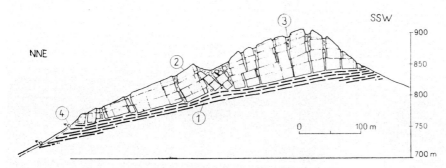

Fig. 10-14. Cambering of Godula Sandstones on the slope of Lukšinec Hill in the Beskydy Mts. (modified from Novosad, 1966); 1 — pelitic beds (predominantly), 2 — sandstones, 3 — gullies, 4 — springs.

by open fissures and gullies filled with loamy debris and loess, their marginal blocks being sunk into the underlying rocks and shifted valleywards. The dissection of travertines is easily observed in a disused quarry at Bešenová near Liptovský Mikuláš, where it seriously aggravated the operation of the quarry.

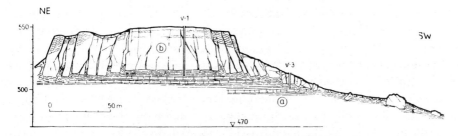

Fig. 10-15. Travertine hillock Dreveník in East Slovakia is cut by deep fissures, along which the marginal blocks sank into the substratum and moved downslope; a — marly shales and sandstones (Palaeogene), b — travertine.

Fig. 10-15 shows a section of the eastern part of the Dreveník travertine mound near Spišské Podhradí, as surveyed in 1950. The Pliocene travertine, up to 35 m thick, rests on the fine-rhythmical flysch which has a dominant pelitic component. Owing to a soft substratum, travertine was gradually torn apart and marginal blocks slipped, tilted and sank partly into the flysch rocks, especially at the southern and eastern margins (Fig. 10-16).

187

Fig. 10-16. Shifted and inclined travertine blocks on the north-eastern slope of Dreveník Hill (photograph by Rubín).

Rocks of flyschoid character accompany the so-called Klippen Belt and are represented by the Cretaceous spherosideritic beds, the Púchov Marlstone and the Palaeogene Flysch. The susceptibility to sliding in the Klippen Belt is encouraged by topographical conditions: blocks and lenses of hard limestone, sandstone or conglomerate, protrude as conspicuous crags and elevations from the soft flyschoid rocks of the klippen mantle. The hard rocks in the upper part of the slopes are resistant to denudation, whereas the soft rocks of the klippen mantle succumb readily to stream erosion. Unstable steep slopes thus developed slide valleywards during the periods rich in rainfall. In the klippen areas, earthflows are the most frequent type of landslides.

Extensive landslides accompany the Klippen Belt from Myjava to the Váh valley and farther to the Orava area and to the Pieniny Mts. Large slides near Dohňany (Fig. 5-9), and Zarječ near Púchov had to be avoided in designing the railway line across the Carpathian ridge. Many landslides threaten the communication running along the Orava river; some of them already needed corrective treatment before the First World War.

Apart from sheet slides and flows of slope debris and waste mantle, in the Orava and Váh valleys even the whole klippen or their parts were set into motion along ancient tectonic surfaces; their sliding was generally provoked by

188

human interference. Thus, for instance, when the Púchov—Horní Lideč railway line was constructed, a cutting was excavated in solid Jurassic limestones thrust on the marly shales of the klippen mantle (Fig. 10-17). The thrust plane

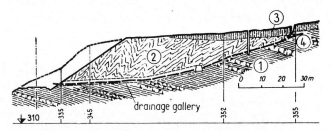

Fig. 10-17. Sliding of Jurassic limestones on an ancient thrust plane, provoked by a railway cutting (near Púchov, Slovakia); 1 — marly shales (Paleogene), 2 — Jurassic limestones, 3 — slope loam, 4 — ancient thrust plane.

dipped valleywards, rising somewhat at the foot of the slope, so that the slope was in an equilibrium state. After its basal part had been broken off, the limestones were no longer supported and started to move down the ancient thrust plane, as might be inferred from the appearance of an open crack in the slope, about 120 m from the axis of the cutting. When the unloading of the upper

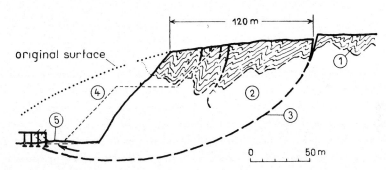

Fig. 10-18. Steep quarry face injured the stability of the whole slope (near Trenčín in Slovakia); 1 — Jurassic limestones, 2 — Púchov marls, 3 — presumed course of the slip surface, 4 — surcharging fill, 5 — squeezed marls at the toe which damaged the new construction (Záruba and Mencl, 1954).

parts proved ineffective, the shape of the ancient thrust plane was examined by means of several galleries. These galleries were then back-filled with stone to increase the friction on the slide plane, and drain the water accumulating at the surface of marly shales.

In the Klippen Belt area the equilibrium of a slope has frequently been disturbed by an unsuitable quarrying procedure. Fig. 10-18 presents the section of a quarry where Jurassic limestones and the Púchov Marls were exploited as raw material for cement production. The 75 m high working face was too steep for the Púchov Marls to preserve their stability. A gaping vertical fissure, formed about 120 m from the upper edge of the face, revealed a strong deformation of the slope due to the squeezing out of the marl at its toe. The movement stopped only after the upper part was unloaded and the bottom of the quarry surcharged.

10.2.2 **Slide areas at the margins of Tertiary volcanic complexes.** In Slovakia, intensive slope movements take place at the periphery of Tertiary effusive sheets covering pelitic rocks of Palaeogene and Neogene age. Sheets of andesite,

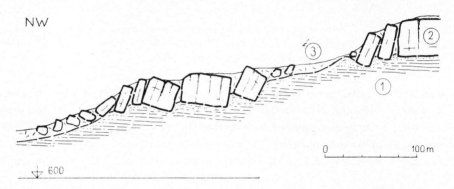

Fig. 10-19. Diagrammatic section of a block slide at the margin of the andesite sheet near Handlová; 1 — Neogene clays and silts, 2 — andesite, 3 — andesite debris.

basalt, liparite and their agglomerates are dissected at the margins into blocks which gradually sink into soft substratum and move valleywards. Blocky and bouldery scree, accumulated below steep marginal walls, overload the upper parts of slope and induce deep landslides in the underlying argillaceous rocks. Many of these block slides date from the Pleistocene; at present they are mostly at rest, unless reactivated by extraordinary climatic conditions or human interference.

Large-size landslides of this type have been observed in the Slovenské rudohorie Mts., at the periphery of the Handlová coal-basin (Fig. 10-19), and at Kordíky near Banská Bystrica. The marginal slopes of the Slanské vrchy Hills (East Slovakia) are affected by deep block slides near Podhradí, Slanec, etc.

10.2.3 **Landslides in the Neogene complexes of the Carpathian Foredeep.** The Carpathian Foredeep developed in the Neogene as a continuous depression rimming the Carpathian arc on the outside. It was filled with marine deposits which were overridden by the marginal flysch parts of the Carpathians during the latest orogenic phase. Neogene marine deposits filling the Upper and Lower

Moravian Basins penetrate through the Moravian Gate into the Ostrava and Opava areas. Soft Neogene rocks, mainly clays, silts, marls and sands with gravel interbeds are responsible for the flattish lowland relief of the region; somewhat steeper slopes are produced only by lateral stream erosion and by man's activity. Sedimentary rocks of the Pannonian basin extending from the Danube Lowland and filling the Váh, Nitra and Hron valleys, show a similar character.

Although the Neogene sediments, especially their pelitic and silty facies are very liable to sliding, natural slides are quite scarce, being limited to the concave banks of major streams. A low strength of rocks motivated slope movements at earlier times, during the development of the moderately undulated relief. Shallow sheet slides disturbing slopes on which clayey rocks crop out are caused mainly by atmospheric agents. Numerous desiccation fissures formed during the dry period facilitate the entry of rainwater into the upper layers and thus contribute to their slaking. Landslides of this kind are known from the surroundings of Hranice, where they threaten the railway line. The sliding near the cement plant at Hranice was also promoted by ground water issuing from the Devonian limestone substratum.

Stream erosion was the motivating force for the origin of landslides on the right bank of the Morava river. The largest slides of this kind occur on the left bank of the Bečva river, at the foot of the Maleník ridge between Hranice and Lipník. Slope loams and debris of the Culm greywackes and shales slip down the northern slope of this elevation over an area about 5 km long and 200 ha in size. In the upper part of the slope several lakelets were ponded (Tyráček, 1959). In Roth's opinion (1962), the Culm block of Maleník is partly thrust on the Neogene of the Moravian Gate, which suggests, as well as the extent of the slide area, that the deformations also involve the marginal Culm blocks.

Any cuttings excavated in Neogene sediments trigger the slope movements. A number of landslides disturbing the railway cuttings may be cited: between Bělotín and Hranice, and at other places on the Brno—Přerov line. Some landslides, originated during the construction of the Brno—Tišnov railway-line, were produced by the ground-water uplift in sand beds (Fig. 7-2). Others may be explained as due to the fissured-clay character of Neogene deposits (see 5.2.1).

Neogene sediments provide favourable conditions for the development of landslides also in the Ostrava and Hlučín areas. All steep slopes, either natural or excavated, are prone to sliding. On the surface of Neogene clays water accumulates, percolates through glacial and fluvioglacial sand and gravel and issuing on the slopes, it disturbs the consistence of Neogene pelitic rocks. Therefore, landslides develop especially on those slopes where the contact of the Quaternary cover and the Neogene beds is exposed; it is generally indicated by a pronounced spring line. The connection of slide phenomena with the Quaternary-Neogene contact has already been mentioned by Götzinger (1909); Žebera (1958) presented a comprehensive list of landslides in the Ostrava area.

The construction of railway lines in the Hlučín area meets with great difficulties. Thus, for instance, a cutting near Petřkovice was designed to reach a depth of 25 m and its lower part should have been excavated in Neogene clays. Yet, as soon as the excavation proceeded into clay deposits, both slopes of the cutting were set into motion and the slipped material had to be removed. The corrective

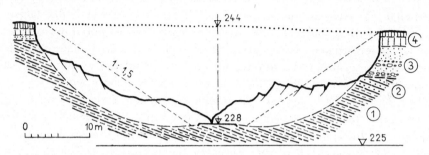

Fig. 10-20. Sliding in a railway cutting near Hlučín, Silesia; 1 — Neogene clays, 2 — crumbly sandstones, 3 — glaciofluvial sands and gravels, 4 — loess-loam (Záruba, 1923).

treatment was directed first to the discharge of water from the horizon on the surface of the Neogene by deep trenches; further, the level of the cutting had to be raised and the angle of the slopes decreased (Fig. 10-20).

10.2.4 Landslides in the Intra-Carpathian depressions. The Intra-Carpathian depressions, comprising the Turiec, Orava and Liptov depressions in the drainage basin of the Váh river, the Žiar and Zvolen depressions in the drainage basin of the Hron river, as well as some others (Nováky—Handlová) that represent the projections of the Pannonian marine basin, are the site of many landslides.

At the base of the basin fill, there is generally a Palaeogene flysch complex of pelitic development, overlain by weakly consolidated Neogene beds of clays, silts and tuffites with gravel interlayers, which in turn are covered by Quaternary deposits (scree, alluvial cones, gravel terraces). The hydrological conditions stemming from the lithological composition of these rocks (a ground-water horizon formed on the surface of impermeable Neogene clays or Palaeogene beds) set the stage for slide movements which may occur wherever steep slopes are produced either by stream erosion or by excavation.

Of a number of slope failures, the disastrous landslide near Handlová (in 1961), sizable sheet slides in the Žiar depression (Kettner 1928), near Súčany in the Turiec depression (Záruba and Mencl, 1958), near Liptovská Mara and Hlohovec in the Váh valley (Lukniš, 1951), and in the railway-cutting near Bánovce (Mencl, 1965b) are worthy of mention. Some of these slide areas date back to the Pleistocene, and the influence of the tectonic subsidence of the depressions (in relation to the adjacent mountain ranges) on their origin cannot

192

be precluded. Even a slight tectonic uplift of the marginal parts had unfavourable effects in that the angle of repose of Neogene beds was increased and stream erosion was revived.

10.2.5 **Landslides in the older geological formations.** In the areas built up of Mesozoic and crystalline rocks, slope movements are, on the whole, quite scarce. Susceptibility to sliding has been observed in the Keuper clayey rocks and the Werfenian beds as far as they display a prevalence of clayey shales. During the construction of the railway line of Diviaky—Banská Bystrica, slide movements of a major extent were provoked in the Žarnovice valley, in places where the Keuper clayey shales crop out in the slope (Fig. 5—8), or near Ulmanka in clayey-sandy debris developed on the Permian sandstones and claystones.

Large rockfalls are known from the Vysoké Tatry (High Tatra) Mts., from their upper slopes glaciated during the Pleistocene. After the retreat of the glacier from the Studená voda valley, for example, huge rockfalls occurred on the eastern slope of Mt. Slavkovský štít. Koutek (1935) described notable rockfalls from the Chočské pohorie Mts. A rockfall in the dolomitic limestones in the Blatná valley, S of Lubochňa, is an exceptional phenomenon. The lake originated by the blocking of the valley still exists.

APPENDIX

As a result of the technique of printing used, it has not been possible to complement this second impression by the addition of the most recent data to a greater extent. The authors are, however, obliged to the Elsevier Publishing Company for affording them the opportunity to at least add appendices to chapters 2 and 6, which briefly mention new opinions on the development of slope failures and some new procedures for the investigation and measurement of movements.

Appendix to Chapter 2

A variety of mechanisms of progressive failure follows from that which has been discussed in sections 2.2 and 2.3. For the sake of lucidity, these mechanisms may be grouped here into several types:

(a) The progressive failure caused by the difference in displacements in rocks and/or soils occurring along the developing slip surface.

(b) The failure caused by a successive onset of new secondary slip surfaces as shown e.g. in Fig. 2–6.

(c) The mechanism of the character of "deep creep" is further discussed on the following pages.

(d) The process of progressive failure due to the existence of residual, inherent stresses in the rock or soil mass (section 2.3).

(e) The delay in the development of sliding movements in clays caused by the slow decrease in strength as a result of consolidation processes (increase in water content) due to removal of a part of the overburden.

(f) The progressive destruction of the slope produced by percolating water as well as by the action of frost.

(g) A progressive redistribution of normal forces due to the displacement of the normal stress along the slip surface (see a slide of the Monte Toc type in Fig. 7–10).

(h) A progressive change of pore-water pressure in the rock or soil mass due to the displacements of the sliding mass.

"Deep creep". The phenomenon of "deep creep" deserves particular attention for two reasons. Its existence has been widely recognized by several engineering geologists (see p. 86) but unfortunately without their considering the mechanical background of the process. By utilizing the widely known facts of volume changes of soils under loading, the analysis is possible and a correlation with the features exhibited by many landslides in clay appears. On the other hand, in spite of the lucidity of the basic properties of materials, the problem of "deep creep" in clay has not been recognized in the analyses of soil mechanics.

In order to understand the mechanical aspects of the phenomenon, four simple facts should be considered:

(1) A thin distinct slip surface develops in a material which has been subjected to a shear stress loading under the condition that the volume of material increases in the course of the shear strain. By analogy, a thick shear zone results from a shear strain accompanied by a decrease in volume. This important phenomenon can be explained on the basis of the principle of the minimum of potential energy and has been discussed elsewhere (Mencl, 1968).

(2) With the exception of loosely packed soils and rocks (e.g., loose sand, weak clay, slope detritus) an increase in volume (dilatancy) is encountered in a shear strained soil or rock mass. Nevertheless, this phenomenon takes place only when the shear strained mass is subjected to a normal pressure below a distinct limit. With normal pressure exceeding this limit, the mass exhibits a decrease in volume (contractancy).

(3) The displacements of the points within or on the surface of a contractant material are many times larger as compared with those met within the dilatant material. This is simply due to the fact that a thick shear zone contributes to the deformations in the former case. Thus, e.g., the displacement of a block in a simple field shear test on Palaeozoic schists was of the order of 1.5 mm when the peak value of resistance was reached. The normal pressure acting on the slip surface was 1.07 kp/cm^2. On the other hand with a normal pressure of 4.57 kp/cm^2, the rock exhibited contractancy and the displacement amounted to 19 mm. As the change in volume due to shear straining begins to appear with shear loadings smaller than the peak resistance, so also the above difference in displacement appears far sooner than the stability failure has been attained.

(4) As explained in the preceding paragraph the deformation of a body exhibiting contractant properties is several times larger than that of a body with dilatant properties. Let us now consider what is the bearing of this behaviour on the phenomenon of creep. When a rock or soil is shear strained by tangential stress which is larger than about 70% of the shear strength, a considerable part of the total deformation does not occur instantaneously but rather proceeds with time. A very slow rate of the time-dependent displacement is termed "creep". The process of creep develops in dilatant as well as in contractant materials. But in dilatant materials the total deformation is relatively small and therefore its time-dependent portion is often small enough to escape the possibility of observation. On the other hand, a contractant material exhibits large deformations and therefore also the creep portion of the latter proceeds in a very distinct way.

There are few records of values of normal pressure under which the dilatant behaviour of rocks changes into the contractant one. This value is the best known for preconsolidated clays and is of the order of 1.5 kp/cm^2. Nevertheless it changes with the degree of preconsolidation as well as with the arrangement of the tests. A value of 5.5 kp/cm^2 has been observed on an argillite of Caradocian age in Prague. The magnitude of the normal stress, of the order of 50 kp/cm^2, can be indicated for mica schist when sheared across the foliation planes.

The consequences of the behaviour of rock and soil masses as described previously are of great importance for landslide phenomena. Let us consider a slope in clay, the stability of which is of the order of 1.1 to 1.2 along a potential slip surface. And let us assume that the central section of the potential slip surface is located at a depth of 10 m below the slope surface. The normal stress induced by the overburden is greater than 1.5 kp/cm². Hence a contractant behaviour of the clay occurs and a thick shear zone begins to develop, accompanied by a relatively large displacement of the overlying mass. On the other hand, the portion of the potential sliding surface adjacent to its upslope exposure is subjected to a much smaller normal stress. Therefore a dilatant behaviour appears and small displacements are to be expected. But the latter portion of the mass is attached to the large central portion downslope which exhibits large displacements. Therefore the upslope portion is carried downslope and a slip surface develops in spite of the fact that the stability of the slope has been greater than one. Moreover, as the phenomenon of creep proceeds in the deep contractant portion of the body, the dilatant portion also displays creep displacements.

The seat of the creep deformations is in the deep contractant portion and therefore the term "deep creep" appears to be adequate. By the very slow displacement of the affected mass, new portions downslope come slowly under the influence of larger normal stress and the mechanism proceeds in a continuous way. The rainwater penetrating into the head scarp may contribute to a deterioration of the slope in a decisive manner.

The phenomena as described in the preceding text constitute one of the most important reasons why the routine statical solutions of the stability of slopes fail.

Appendix to Chapter 6

The determination of the depth of the sliding surface (6.1.1.) is difficult in stabilized landslides, and in the first stages of slope failures when the movements have the character of creeping or very slow shear deformation (rates of several mm to cm per year) within a zone of decimetre to metre-thickness. As the above described measurements of borehole distortion would provide reliable information of the position of the slide surface only after several months or years of observation, some other methods are being developed.

In the U.S.S.R. the depth of the slide surfaces in deep-reaching landslides is determined, at their initial stage, in the following way: steel bands, 4 cm wide, are installed in drill-holes filled with sand. The bands are put under tension by suspended weights and their degree of bending is measured by the use of a system of resistivity tensometers which are attached to them.

The slow movements of the sliding rock mass lead to increase in stress above the elasticity limit, which results in permanent deformation up to rupture of the rock. In the stressed rock, subaudible acoustic impulses within the sound spectrum are generated. These noises are of the greatest intensity and frequency in the close proximity of the slide surface. This phenomenon may be utilized for the determination of the slide surface or zone even before the shear failure has taken place. The impulses are picked up by an array of sensitive geophones lowered into a borehole and after amplification they are registered on a tape recorder. A graphic record is obtained using an oscillograph, and from it the seismo-acoustic activity, intensity and frequency of impulses are evaluated. The segment of the borehole showing the maximum seismo-acoustic activity (frequency maximum of impulses in the time unit) is then identified with the true or potential slide zone. This technique which has been commonly used for some time in mining and other underground works, found little application until recently in the location of the seat of sliding.

The method was developed for this purpose by R.E. Goodman and W. Blake in the U.S.A. and simultaneously by workers of the VSEGINGEO Institute in the U.S.S.R.

The rock-noise monitoring is time saving and the experienced worker is able to identify fairly confidently the slide surface from the relative noise rates in a borehole through the slide. The suitable layout of test holes over extensive stabilized landslides makes it possible to delimit the parts prone to the revived movements called forth by natural or human interference with the stability conditions. Care must be taken, however, to eliminate background noise which may override any impulses generated by sliding.

As the slide surfaces are generally distinguished by an increased moisture of the rocks, the methods of geophysical logging may be used successfully for their establishment. Resistivity and neutron logging are particularly suitable for this purpose. The latter is capable of determining the moisture content in homogeneous clayey rocks with a sufficient degree of accuracy.

In some rock complexes the slide surface develops on a thin clay layer. When the boring passes through the slide surface, the clay is squeezed into the hole. The segments where the clay penetrates inside can be established with the use of a device measuring the widening or constriction of the bore profile. Photographic and TV cameras are also suitable for the inspection of the walls of a borehole.

In landslides reaching to great depths, the excavation of exploration pits and galleries and the drilling of the holes is cumbersome and expensive. Under certain conditions these subsurface works are supplemented by indirect geophysical methods in order to locate the slide surface with a greater precision.

Resistivity logging is a suitable method for the determination of the slide zone in rock material, when this is developed as a kneaded clay layer distinguished by low specific resistivity. It can also be employed to advantage in landslides along predetermined surfaces, when these coincide with the boundaries between rocks of different specific resistivity, as for example, between the bedrock and superficial deposits.

When a landslide occurs in solid rocks, the displaced masses become loosened and disrupted by open cracks and fissures. Such a disturbance is manifested by a marked drop in the velocity of seismic-wave propagation. This phenomenon is utilized in seismic measurements; from the differences in the velocity of seismic waves, the surface of rocks unaffected by slope movements is readily determined. The seismic refraction method is particularly convenient for this purpose. In landslides of small or medium depth, impacts of a hammer or a weight are used as sources of vibrations; in deeper landslides seismic waves are produced by blasting with small charges of explosives.

The combined seismic and seismo-acoustic methods make it possible to estimate the degree of stability of a landslide from the changes in seismo-acoustic activity, increased or provoked by blasting. In the landslides of a labile equilibrium state, the increase of seismo-acoustic activity provoked by blasting a small charge declines gradually, whereas in the stabilized landslides this activity ceases immediately after the explosion.

The test pits sunk down to the solid ground under the slid masses (6.1.6) may be employed for the observation of slope movements at depth. The pits are provided with a suitable (commonly concrete) casing with gravel backfilling. The low-rate movements are measured with a pendulum arrangement similar to that used for the measurement of the inclinations of dam walls. The pendulum is suspended on the casing above the slide surface and the reading device is fixed under this surface. The horizontal components of the movement are measured with an accuracy of tenths of a millimetre.

In certain types of rocks the so-called block landslides are a frequent phenomenon. The displacement of adjacent blocks can be measured with the use of dilatometric cramps which are currently used for the detection of deformations in dams.

In Czechoslovakia a new type of extensometer has been developed for the direct measurement of very small long-term movements in the fossil block landslides (Košťák, 1969). The device was designed using the Moiré technique, which provides the possibility of detection of movement from the fringe patterns produced by grids displaced relative to each other. The extensometer consists of two rigid holders and two Moiré units, i.e., two pairs of metal plates with glass spiral grids. The holders are fixed in the facing walls of the joints between the blocks; the units are mounted on the edge plates of the holders, the upper unit in the horizontal position and the lower in the vertical position. The displacement is thus detectable on two planes perpendicular to each other, and it is evaluated from the total number of fringes. The readings can be made either visually or by photographs. The sensitivity and accuracy of the instrument depend on the density of the grids. It may record the movement in any direction with accuracy of about 0.1 mm.

References

Bůžková, H., Müller, K., Novosad, S., 1969. K metodice průzkumu skalních sesuvů v Moravskoslezských Beskydech. Geol. průzkum 2.

Cadman, I.D., Goodman, R.E., Van Alstine, Ch., 1967. Research on subaudible noise in landslides. University of California, Berkeley, Calif., 94 pp.

Goodman, R.E., Blake, W., 1965. An investigation of rock noise in landslides and cut slopes. Rock Mechanics a. Eng. Geol. 3, Suppl. 2: 88–93.

Košťák, B., 1969. A new device for in situ movement detection and measurement. Exp. Mech., 1969: 374–379.

Mencl, V., 1968. Panel Discussion. Proc., Geotech. Conf., Oslo, 1967. Norwegian Geotech. Inst., Oslo, 2: 231–232.

VSEGINGEO Inst., 1969. Glubynnye opolznevye repery. Moskva. Min. geologii.

Bibliography

AGARD, M., 1948. Les glissements et éboulement des quartiers St. Raphaël et Télemly à Alger. Annales des Ponts et Chaussées, 118: 465–480, Paris.

ALEKSEENKO, E. YA., 1964. Metodika deshifrovaniya opolznevykh yavlenii po materialam aerofotosemki. Aerometody pro poiskakh poleznykh iskopaemykh i geologicheskom kartirovanii. AN SSSR, Moskva.

ALMAGIÀ, R., 1910. Studi geografici sulle frane in Italia. Soc. Geogr. Italiana, Roma, 342 pp.

AMPFERER, O., 1939. Über einige Formen der Bergzerreissung. Sitzungsber. Akad. Wiss. Wien, 148: 1–14.

— 1940. Zum weiteren Ausbau der Lehre von den Bergzerreissungen. Sitzungsber. Akad. Wiss. Wien, 149: 51–70.

ANDERSSON, L. G., 1906. Solifluction, a component of subaerial denudation. Journal Geol. 14: 91–112.

ANDRUSOV, D., 1931. Poznámka o sesuvech v povodí Oravy na Slovensku. Věstník st. geol. ústavu, 7: 172–174.

AYRES, D. J., 1961. The treatment of unstable slopes and railway track formations. Journal Soc. of Eng., 52: 111–138.

BAJTOŠ, G., 1961. Geodetické pozorovacie práce na zosuve v Handlovej. Manuscript, Ústav geodézie a kartografie v Žiline.

BAKER, R. F., 1952. Determining corrective action for highway landslide problems. Highway Research Board, Bull. 49, Washington, 39 pp.

— 1953. Analysis of corrective actions for highway landslides. Proceedings Am. Soc. of Civ. Eng., 79.

— 1959. Regional concept of landslide occurrence. Highway Research Board Bull. 216, Washington.

BALTZER, A., 1875. Über Bergstürze in den Alpen. Schweizer Alpenclub, 10: 409–456. Bern.

BELES, A. A., 1957. Le traitment thermique du sol. In: Proc. 4th Intern. Conf. Soil. Mech. and Found. Eng., 3: 266–267.

BRAIT, P. I., 1964: Geodezicheskie metody izmereniya smeshchenii na opolznyakh. Izd. NEDRA, Moskva.

BENSON, W. N., 1940. Landslides and applied features in the Dunedin District in relation to geological structure, topography and engineering. Roy. Soc. New Zealand Trans., 70: 249–263.

— 1946. Landslides and their relation to engineering in the Dunedin District, New Zealand. Economic Geology, 41: 328–347.

BERNATZIK, W., 1957. Baugrund und Physik. Schweizer Druck- und Verlagshaus, Zürich, 310 pp.

BISHOP, A. W., 1955. The use of the slip circle in the stability analysis of slopes. Géotechnique, 5: 7–17.

BISHOP, A. W., MORGENSTERN, N., 1960. Stability coefficients for earth slopes. Géotechnique, 10: 129–150.

BJERRUM, L., 1955. Stability of natural slopes in quick clay. Norwegian Geotechn. Inst. Oslo, 19 pp.

— 1966. Mechanism of progressive failure in slopes of overconsolidated plastic clays and clay shales. Norwegian Geotechn. Inst., Oslo, 67 pp.

BJERRUM, L., JÖRSTAD, F., 1966. Stability of rock slopes in Norway. Norwegian Geotechn. Inst., Oslo, 67 : 50—78.

BLACKWELDER, E., 1912. The Gros Ventre slide, an active earth-flow. Bull. Geol. Soc. Am., 23: 487—492.

— 1928. Mudflow as geologic agent in semiarid mountains. Bull. Geol. Soc. Am., 39: 465—480.

BRABEC, S., 1962. Sanace sváživého území metodou Aerocem v jílovité zemině. Železniční doprava a technika, 10: 342—344.

BROWN, C. B., 1938. On a theory of gravitational sliding applied to the Tertiary of Ancon, Ecuador. Quart. Jour. Geol. Soc., 94: 359—370.

BUXTORF, A., 1922. Das Längenprofil des schweizerisch-französischen Doubs zwischen dem Lac des Brenets und Soubey. Eclogae Geol. Helvetiae, 16: 527—537.

CAPRA, U., LINARI, C., 1960. I movimenti della massa rocciosa sulla sponda sinistra del serbatoio di Pontesei. Geotecnica, 7 : 118—124, Milano.

CASAGRANDE, L., 1941. Die elektrische Entwässerung feinkörniger Böden. Die Strasse: 324—326.

CASAGRANDE, L., LOUGHNEY, R. W., MATICH, M. A. I., 1961. Electro-osmotic stabilization of a high slope in loose saturated silt. Proceed. of the 5. Intern. Conf. on Soil Mech. and Found. Eng., 2: 555—561, Paris.

ČERMÁK, K., 1912. Sesutí stráně a hrazené jezero u Mladotic. Sborník Čes. spol. zeměvědné 18: 19—23.

CHURINOV, M. V., 1957. Kharakteristika opolznei pravogo berega r. Moskvy na uchastke Leninskikh gor i vozmozhnost stroitelnogo osvoeniya etoi territorii. Voprosy gidrogeol. i inzhenernoi geol., 15: 62—78, Moskva.

CLAR, E., 1963. Gefüge und Verhalten von Felskörpern in geologischer Sicht. Rock Mechanics a. Eng. Geol. 1: 4—15.

CLAR, E., WEISS, P., 1965. Erfahrungen im Talzuschub des Magnesit-Bergbaues auf der Millstätter Alpe. Berg- und Hüttenmännische Monatshefte, 110: 447—460.

DĚDINA, V., 1926. Sesouvání půdy na úbočí Mužského u Mnichova Hradiště. Sborník Čs. společnosti zeměpisné, 32: 192—195.;

DENISOV, N. J., 1951. Oznachenii svyazannoj vlagi v deformaciyakh glinistykh porod. Gidr. Stroitelstvo.

DOW, R. B., 1956. Some rheological properties under high pressure. Rheology 1, Acad. Press, New York.

DRAGOS, V., 1957. Deplasari de teren. Editura stiintifica, Bucuresti, 162 pp.

DREYER, W., 1963. Die Bedeutung der Festigkeit des Gebirges im Kali- und Steinsalzbergbau. Berichte Ländertreffen I. B. G. Leipzig.

DROUHIN, G., GAUTIER, M., DERVIEUX, F., 1948. Slide and subsidence of the hills of St. Rafael-Télemly. Proc. of the II. Intern. Conf. on Soil Mech. and Found. Eng. 5: 104, 106.

ECKEL, E. B., 1958. (Editor) Landslides and engineering practice. Highway Research Board, Spec. Rep. 29, NAS-NRC 544. Washington, 232 pp.

EMELYANOVA, J. P., 1953. O prichinakh i faktorekh opolznevykh protsesov. Voprosy gidrogeol. i inzhenernoi geol., Moskva.

— 1956. Metodicheskoe rukovodstvo po statsionarnomu izucheniyu opolznei. Gosgeoltekhizdat, Moskva, 245 pp.

EMERSON, F. B., 1925. 80-Foot dam formed by landslide in Gros Ventre Canyon, Wyoming. Eng. News-Record, 95: 467—468.

FELLENIUS, M., 1927. Erdstatische Berechnungen mit Reibung und Kohäsion und unter Annahme kreiszylindrischer Gleitflächen. Ernst u. Sohn, Berlin, 40 pp.

FELT, J. E., 1953. Influence of vegetation on soil moisture contents and resulting soil volume changes. Proc. 1, 3rd Intern. Conf. Soil Mech. and Found. Eng., Zürich.

FENCL, J., 1966. Typy sesuvů v české křídové pánvi. Sborník geol. věd, HIG, 5: 23—41.

FENCL, J., ZÁRUBA, Q., 1956. Geologické poměry okolí Lázní Teplic v Čechách. Sborník ÚÚG, 22: 427—484.

FINZI, D., VEDER, C., 1962. Stabilizzatione di una frana mediante infissione di elettrodi nel piano di scivolamento. Geotecnica, 9: 194—200.

FISCHER, A., 1930. Sesuvy železničního tělesa dráhy Rakovník—Louny a sanace těchto sesuvů. Technický obzor, 38: 329—336.

FORBES, H., 1947. Landslide investigations and corrections. A. S. C. E. Trans., 112: 377—442. New York.

GIANNINI, E., 1951. Alloctonia del macigno nella regione Bagni di Casciana-Chianni in provincia di Pisa, Boll. Soc. Geol. It., 70.

GIGNOUX, M., BARBIER, R., 1955. Géologie des barrages et des aménagements hydrauliques. Masson & Cie. Paris, 339 pp.

GÖTZINGER, G., 1907. Beiträge zur Entstehung der Bergrückenformen. Geograph. Abhandl., 9: 1—174.

— 1909. Geologische Studien im subbeskidischen Vorland auf Blatt Freistadt in Schlesien. Jahrb. d. k. k. Geol. Reichsanstalt, Wien.

— 1943. Neue Beobachtungen über Bodenbewegungen in der Flyschzone. Mitteil. der Geograph. Gesell., 86, Wien.

GOULD, J. P., 1960. A study of shear failure of certain Tertiary marine sediments. Conf. Shear Strength of Cohesive Soils, A. S. C. E.

GRIGGS, D., 1939. Creep of rocks, Jour. Geol. 47 (3).

HADDING, A., 1931. On subaqueous slides. Geol. Fören. Stockh. Förh., 53: 377—393.

HAEFELI, R., 1944. Zur Erd- und Kriechdruck-Theorie. Schweiz. Bauzeit., 124.

HAEFELI, R., 1953. Creep problems in soils, snow and ice. Proc. of the 3rd Intern. Conf. on Soil Mech. and Found. Eng., 3: 238—251. Zürich.

HARRISON, J. V., FALCON, N. L., 1936. Gravity collapse structures and mountain ranges, as exemplified in south-western Persia. Quart. Jour. Geol. Soc. London, 92: 91—102.

HAST, N., 1958. The measurement of rock pressures in mines. Sveriges Geologiska Undersöning Arsbok, 52: 181—183.

— 1964. Recent rock pressure measurements and their implications for dam building. Trans. 8. Intern. Congress on Large Dams, 1. Edinburgh.

HEIM, A., 1882. Der Bergsturz von Elm. Zeitschr. der Deutsch. geol. Ges., 34: 74—110.

— 1895. Der diluviale Bergsturz von Glärnisch-Guppen. Vierteljahrsschrift d. naturf. Ges. in Zürich, 40: 1—32.

— 1908. Über rezente und fossile subaquatische Rutschungen und deren lithologische Bedeutung. Neues Jahrb. f. Mineral., Geol. u. Paleont., 2: 136—157.

— 1919/1921/1922. Geologie der Schweiz. Tauchnitz Leipzig, 1118 pp.

— 1932. Bergsturz und Menschenleben. Naturf. Gesell., Zürich, Vierteljahrschrift, 77: 218.

HEIM, A., BUSS, E., 1881. Der Bergsturz von Elm. Zürich, 163 pp.

HERLINGER, E. W., STAFFORD, G., 1952. Orinda Slide. Calif. Highways and Public Works, 31: 45—52.

HIBSCH, J. E., 1903. Erläut. zu Blatt Grosspriesen, Geolog. Karte des Böhmischen Mittelgebirges, Wien.

— 1904. Erläut. zu Blatt Aussig, Geolog. Karte des Böhmischen Mittelgebirges, Wien.

— 1917. Erläut. zu Blatt VIII, Salesel, Wien.

205

HOLLINGWORTH, S. E., TAYLOR, J. H., 1944. Large-scale superficial structures in the Northampton Ironstone Field. Quart. Journ. of. Geol. Soc. London, 100: 1—44.

HOLMSEN P., 1953. Landslip in Norwegian quickclays. Géotechnique, 3: 187—194.

HOUSKA, J., 1963. Zkoušky pevnosti hornin v laboratoři. In: Metodika inž. geol. výzkumu pevných hornin. Academia, Praha, pp. 50—74.

HOWE, E., 1909. Landslides in the San Juan Mountains, Colorado. U. S. Geol. Survey, 67, 58 pp.

ILIE, M., 1955. Cercetari geologice in Bazinul Transilvaniei. An. Com. Geol., 28: 354—358. Bucuresti.

JEDLIČKA, M., TKANÝ, Z., 1965. Odvodnění sesuvu horizontálními vrty. Inženýrské stavby č. 3.

KAZDA, J., 1960. Chemické ovlivňování bobtnavosti jílovitých zemin. Sborník VÚT, Brno, p. 243—255.

— 1961a. Nowe metody badawcze w gruntoznawstwie inzynieryjnym. Soil Mech. and Found. Eng. Conference, Wrocław.

— 1961b. Vliv druhu sorbovaných kationtů na fysikální a mechanické vlastnosti jílovitých zemin. Colloq. Miner. geolog. Society, Brno.

KEIL, K., 1951. Ingenieurgeologie und Geotechnik. Knapp, Halle (Saale), 1065 pp.

KENNEY, T. C., 1961. Corresp. Géotechnique, 11: 54—55.

KETTNER, R., 1928. Příspěvek k poznání geolog. poměrů hronské kotliny svätokrižské. Rozpravy Čes. akad. 37, 19 pp. Praha.

KIERSCH, G. A., 1964. Vaiont reservoir disaster. Civil Eng., 34: 32—39.

KIESLINGER, A., 1958. Restspannung und Entspannung im Gestein. Geologie u. Bauwesen, 24: 95—112.

KJELLMANN, W., 1955. Mechanics of large Swedish landslides. Geotechnique, 5, No. 1.

KNORRE, M. E., ABRAMOV, S. K., ROGOZIN, I. S., 1951. Opolzni i mery borby s nimi. Moskva.

KOUTEK, J., 1935. Geologická mapa Prosečnických hor a přilehlých oblastí flyšových. Věstník stát. geol. ústavu, 11: 115—127.

KRAUS, J., KUBÍČEK, B., 1963. Sanace sváživých svahů injektováním. Inženýrské stavby, 11: 151—155.

KRAUS, J., TYC, P., 1965. Sanace železničních násypů a zářezů. Nakl. dopravy a spojů, Praha, 367 pp.

KREJČÍ, J., 1943. Sesuvná území na Zlínsku. Práce Moravské přírodovědecké spol., Brno, 22 pp.

KŘIVANEC, F., 1901. Ausgeführte Entwässerungen von Erdrutschungen. Österr. Wochenschrift f. d. öffentl. Baudienst., Wien.

KRYNINE, D. P., 1960. On the methodology of landslide investigations in Soviet Russia. Highway Research Board Bull. 236, Washington.

KSIĄŻKIEWICZ, M., 1958a. Osuwiska podmorskie we fliszu Karpackim. Rocz. Pol. Tow. Geol. Kraków, 28: 123—152.

— 1958b. Sedimentation in the Carpathian Flysch Sea. Geol. Rundschau, 47: 418—425.

LADD, G. E., 1935. Landslides, subsidences and rockfalls. Proc. Am. Railw. Eng. Assoc., 36: 1091—1162.

LEGGET R. F., 1962. Geology and engineering. McGraw-Hill, New York, 884 pp.

LESŇÁK, O., 1963. Zjišťování mechanických vlastností hornin Schmidtovým kladivem. Report V. U. U. Ostrava.

v. LINSTOW, O., 1929. Bodenanzeigende Pflanzen. Abhandl. der Preuss. Geol. Landesanstalt, H. 114. Berlin.

LITVINOV, I. M., 1955. Termicheskoe ukreplenie prosadochnykh lessovykh i drugikh gruntov v osnovanijakh razlichnykh zdanii i sooruzhenii, Izd. Akad. Arkhitektury Ukrainskoi SSR. Kiev.

LOŽEK, V., PROŠEK, F., 1957. Krasové zjevy v travertinech a jejich stratigrafický význam. Čsl. kras 10: 145—158.

206

LUKNIŠ, M., 1951. Sesuvné území na lavom brehu Váhu medzi Hlohovcom a Šintavou. Zemepisný sborník SAV, 3: 53—77.

MASLOV, N. N., 1955. Usloviya ustoichivosti sklonov i otkosov v gidroenergicheskom stroitelstve. Moskva.

MATULA, M., MODLITBA, I., PINKA, V., 1965. K rozvoju zosuvných procesov v Západných Karpatoch. Acta Geol. et Geograph. Univ. Comenianae, Bratislava, 10: 69—88.

MATULA, M., NEMČOK, A., 1966. Prehlad zosuvných procesov na Slovensku. Inženýrské stavby, 14: 29—30.

MATULA, M., NEMČOK, A., PAŠEK, J., ŘEPKA, L., ŠPŮREK, M., 1963. Sesuvná území ČSSR. Manuscript, Geofond, Praha.

McCONNELL, R. G., BROCK, R. W., 1904. Great landslides at Frank, Alberta. Canada Dept. Inter. Ann. Rept., 17 pp.

MENCL, V., 1953. Některé zjevy z mechaniky zemin při stavbě železničního spodku. Seminář Železnič. staveb. IV ČVUT, Praha.

— 1955. Mechanika zemin. NČSAV Praha, 255 pp.

— 1961. Panel discussion on Rock Mechanics. Compt. Ren. Congr. Intern. Méc. Sols-Trav. Fond., III, Paris.

— 1962a. Zpráva o sesuvech v Bánovcích. Report VUT, Brno.

— 1962b. Měření napjatosti v měkkých horninách. Věstník ÚÚG, 27: 209—212.

— 1964. Discussion. Géotechnique, 14/1: 59—60.

— 1965a. Three questions on the stability of slopes. Proceed. Intern. Conf. Soil Mech. Found. Eng., Montreal 2: 512—513.

— 1965b. Stability of slopes. Discussion, Proceed. Internat. Conf. Soil Mech. Found. Eng., Montreal 3: 550—551.

— 1966a. Mechanika zemin a skalních hornin. Academia, Praha, 329 pp.

— 1966b. Die Ausbildung der Scherzone bei der mehrachsigen Beanspruchung des Karbongebirges. Referat, 8. Ländertreffen Int. Büro Gebirgsmechanik, Leipzig.

— 1966c. Mechanics of landslides with non-circular slip surfaces with special reference to the Vaiont Slide. Géotechnique, 16: 329—337.

— 1966d. The influence of the stiffness of a sliding mass on the stability of slopes. Rock Mechanics and Eng. Geol., 4: 127—131.

MENCL, V., NĚMCOVÁ, S., 1965. Stabilita komunikačních násypů v zdržích přehrad. Inž. stavby, 4: 176—180.

MENCL, V., TRÁVNÍČEK, I., 1964. Relaxationsversuche am Gebirge. 6. Ländertreffen I. B. G., Leipzig.

MIGNON, K., 1962. Ergebnisse der geol. Stollenaufnahme für das Lünerseewerk, Vorarlberg. Jb. Geol. B. A., 105, p. 49—64, Wien.

MOOR, R., 1923. Der Uferabbruch am Davoser See. Schweizer. Bauzeit. 82.

v. MOOS, A., RUTSCH, R. F., 1944. Über einen durch Gefügestörung verursachten Seeufereinbruch Eclogae Geol. Helv., 37/2.

MORTIER, P., 1964. Étude expérimentale de la déformation des roches. Doct. Thesis, Univ. de Paris.

MOUM, J., ROSENQVIST, I. TH., 1957. On the weathering of young marine clays. Conf. Int. Soc. Soil Mech. Found. Eng., London, 1: 77—79.

MÜLLER, L., 1963a. Die Standfestigkeit von Felsböschungen als spezifisch geomechanische Aufgabe. Rock Mechanics a. Eng. Geol., 1: 50—71.

— 1963b. Der Felsbau. Enke Ver. Stuttgart, 624 pp.

— 1964. The rock slide in the Vaiont valley. Rock Mechanics a. Eng. Geol., 2: 148—212.

MYSLIL, V., ŠILAR, J., 1953. Proudový sesuv u Radotína. Věstník ÚÚG, 28: 83—90.

MYSLIVEC, A., 1951. Sváženi silničních svahů a jejich zabezpečení. ČVUT, Praha, 26 pp.

NÄGELI, H., 1920. Die postglazial-prähistorischen Biashina-Bergstürze. Vierteljahrschrift d. Naturf. Ges. Zürich, 65: 1—58.

NEMČOK, A., 1964. Geological construction of slopes and its influence on the origin and distribution of landslides in the West Carpathians. Geologický sborník SAV, Bratislava, 15.

— 1966. Vývoj zosuvných území na rozhraniach geologických útvarov. Sborník geol. věd, HIG, 5: 87—105.

NĚMEC, B., BABIČKA, J., OBORSKÝ, A., 1936. Výskyt zlata v přesličkách. Rozpravy Čes. Akad., Praha.

NEUMAYR, M., 1889. Über Bergstürze. Zeitschr. d. Deutsch. u. Öster. Alpenver., 20: 19—56.

NOVÁK, F., 1964. Zkušenosti a poznatky z tepelného zpevňování zemin. Inž. stavby, 12: 473—479.

NOVOSAD, S., 1966. Porušení svahů v godulských vrstvách Moravskoslezských Beskyd. Sborník geol. věd, HIG, 5: 71—86.

OBERHOLZER, J., 1933. Geologie der Glarneralpen. Beiträge zur Geol. Karte der Schweiz. Bern.

PALMER, L. A., THOMPSON, J. B., YEOMANS, C. M., 1950. The control of a landslide by surface drainage. Highway Research Board, Proc., 30.

PALSHIN, G. B., 1963. Opolzni. In: Bratskoe vodokhranilishche, Izd. Akad. Nauk SSSR, Moskva, pp. 130—152.

PAŠEK, J., 1957. Fosilní sesuv na Váhu. Věstník ÚÚG, 32: 47—60.

— 1967. Schollenartige Hangbewegungen. Mitt. Ges. Geol. Bergbaustud., Wien, 18: 369—378.

PENTA, F., 1960a. Frane e movimenti franosi. Università degli studi di Roma, Roma. 208 pp.

— 1960b. Lame e creep. Geotecnica, 7: 67—77.

PETRÁNEK, J., 1963. Usazené horniny. Academia, Praha, 718 pp.

PETRÁŠEK, J., ZÁRUBA, Q., 1959. Použitie geodetických metód pre sledování pohybu na zosuvnom území medzi Sučanmi a Klačanmi. Staveb. čas. SAV, 7: 33—42.

POČTA, F., 1915. O sjíždění půdy v sev. Čechách. Slavnostní spis čes. akad., k 70. naroz. prof. K. Vrby, Praha.

POLÁK, V., 1965. Výzkum přetvárných vlastností a podmínek porušení hornin. Zpráva Hornického ústavu ČSAV, Praha.

POLLACK, V., 1918. Über Rutschungen im Glazialen und die Notwendigkeit einer Klassifikation loser Massen. Jahrb. der k. k. Geol. Reichsanstalt, 67: 435—460.

POPOV, I. V., 1951. Inzhenernaya geologiya. Gos. izd. geol. lit. Moskva, pp. 442.

PROIX-NOÉ, M., 1946. Étude d'un glissement de terrain du à la présence de glauconie. Compt. rend. Acad. sci., 222: 403—405.

v. RABCEWICZ, L., 1957. Die Ankerung im Tunnelbau ersetzt bisher gebräuchliche Einbaumethoden. Schweizer. Bauzeit., 75.

REINER, M., 1958. Rheology. Handbuch der Physik B VI, Springer Verlag.

REUSCH H., 1901. Norwegian geological Survey, 32: 218—226.

REUTER, F., 1958. Hangrutschungen bei den Baustellen des Bodeswerkes. Zeitschr. für angewandte Geol., 2/3: 94—98.

ROBERTS, A., et al., 1964. The determination of the strength of rock in situ. Trans. 8. Internat. Cong. on Large Dams Edinburgh, 1: 167—186.

ROGOZIN, I. S., 1958. Volzhskie opolzni, Akad. nauk. SSSR. Moskva.

— 1961. Opolzni Ulyanovska i opyt borby s nimi. Akad. nauk SSSR. Moskva.

RÖHLICH, P., 1963. Podmořské skluzy a bahnotoky v nejmladším středočeském algonkiu. Sborník geol. věd G., 6: 89—121.

ROSENQVIST, I., TH., 1953. Consideration on the sensitivity of Norwegian quick clays. Norwegian Geot. Inst., Oslo.

ROTH, Z., 1944. Skalní proudy, ledovcové kary a ledovce. Rozpravy čs. akad., Praha.

— 1945. Stabilita skalních zářezů a tlaky při ražení štol v pevných horninách. Technický obzor, 53: 201—288, 312—315.

— 1962. Vysvětlivky k přehledné geologické mapě ČSSR 1 : 200.000, list Olomouc. Geofond, Praha.

Rybář, J., 1961. Shrnutí vrstev na okraji hnědouhelné pánve u Kadaně. Věstník ÚÚG, 36: 223—227.

— 1968. Ein Beispiel von Bewegungsmessungen an Rutschungen. Zeitschr. f. angewandte Geol., 14: 138—141.

Rybář, J., Pašek, J., Řepka, L., 1965. Dokumentation der systematischen Untersuchung der Rutschungsgebiete in der Tschechoslowakei. Engineering Geology, 1: 21—29.

Sander, B., 1948. Einführung in die Gefügenkunde. Springer, Wien.

Savarenskii, P. F., 1937. Inzhenernaya geologiya. Moskva.

Sawicki, L., 1917. Osuwisko ziemne w Szymbarku i inne zsuwy powstale w r. 1913 w Galicyi zachodniej. Akad. Um., Kraków, 89 pp.

Segré, C., 1924. Condizioni geognostico-costructive di due grandi sbarramenti nell Appennino Emiliano. Roma.

Selli, R., Trevisan, L., et al., 1964. La frana del Vaiont. Annali del Museo geologico di Bologna, 32, 68 pp.

Sharpe, C. F. S., 1938. Landslides and related phenomena. Columbia Univ. Press, New York, 137 pp.

Sintsov, L., 1898. Ob odesskikh opolzniyakh i o prichinakh ikh proiskhozhdeniya. Zap. Novoros. Obch. Estestv., Odesa. 22: 187—241.

Sitter de, L. V., 1956. Structural Geology. McGraw-Hill, New York, 552 pp.

Skatula, L., 1953. Hrazení bystřin a strží. Praha.

Skempton, A. W., 1946. Earth pressure and the stability of slopes. The Instit. of Civil. Eng., London.

— 1948. A possible relationship between true cohesion and the mineralogy of clays. Proc. Second Int. Conf. Soil Mech. and Found. Eng., 7: 45. Rotterdam.

— 1953. "The colloidal activity" of clays. Proc. 3rd Int. Conf. Soil Mech. Found. Eng., 1: 57—61, Zürich.

Skutta, E., 1963. Planmässige gesteinsmechanische Untersuchungen des Schichtenverbands von Karbongesteinen. Dissert. Tech. Hochschule, Aachen.

Smith, R., Peck, R. B., 1955. Stabilization by pressure grouting on American railroads. Géotechnique, 5: 243—252.

Snow, D. T., 1964. Landslide of Cerro Condor-Sencca, Department of Ayacucho, Peru. Eng. Geology Case Histories, No. 5, 1—6, New York.

Stanculescu, J., 1962. Sicherung der Geländerrutschung im Stadtgebiet von Konstanza (Rumänische Volksrepublik). Wissen. Zeitsch. d. Techn. Univ. Dresden, 12: 489—499.

Statens Järnvågars Geotekniska Kommission, Slutbetänkande. Stockholm 1932, 180 pp.

Stejskal, J., 1931. Svážná území na Pavlovských vrších. Sborník čsl. akd. zeměděl., 6: 55—94.

— 1935. Geologická stavba Pavlovských vrchů. Věstník stát. geol. ústavu, 11: 15—32.

— 1939. Sesouvání půdy na Hazmburku u Klapého. Praha.

Stiny, J., 1910. Die Muren. Wagner, Insbruck, 139 pp.

— 1929. Zur Kenntnis und Abwehr der Rutschungen. Geol. u. Bauw., 1: 190—201.

— 1941. Unsere Täler wachsen zu. Geol. u. Bauw., 13: 71—79.

Sýkora, L., 1961. Fytoindikace sesuvných území v ČSSR. Rozpravy ČSAV, 71, 61 pp.

Talobre, M. I., 1957. La mécanique des roches. Dunod, Paris, 444 pp.

Ter-Stepanian, G. I., 1958. Klassifikatsiya opolznevykh treshchin. Izv. Akad. Nauk Armyanskoi SSR, IX, 5.

— 1965. Über den Mechanismus des Hakenwerfens. Felsmechanik u. Ingenieurgeologie, III/2.

Terzaghi, K., 1950. Mechanics of landslides. In: Geol. Soc. of Am., Berkey Volume, New York, pp. 83—124.

— 1960. Stability of steep slopes on hard unweathered rock. Géotechnique, 12: 251–270.

— 1962. Does foundation technology really lag? Eng. News-Record, p. 58–59.

TERZAGHI, K., PECK, R. B., 1948. Soil mechanics in engineering practice. Willey & sons, New York, 566 pp.

TOMS, A. H., 1946. Folkestone Warren landslips. Inst. Civil Eng. Railw. Eng. Div., 19, London.

TRZHTSINSKII, YU. B., 1964. Opolzni v doline rek Ilima i srednei Angary. In: Materialy Sov. vop. izucheniya opolznei i mer borby s nimi. Kiev, pp. 129–132.

TSYTOVICH, N. A., 1951. Mekhanika gruntov. Gos. Izd. liter. po stroit. i arkhitekture, Moskva, 528 pp.

TYRÁČEK, J., 1959. Území topografické sekce 4159/4 mezi Drahušovicemi a Bělotínem. Anthropozoikum, Praha, 8: 273–276.

UNDERWOOD, L. B., 1964. Chalk foundation at four major dams in the Missouri River Basin. Trans. 8. Internat. Cong. on Large Dams, 1, R_2. Edinburgh.

URYCH, R., 1927. Svážná území. Techn. obzor, 62: 57–59.

VARNES, D. J., 1950. Relation of landslides to sedimentary features. In: Applied sedimentation, J. Wiley & sons, New York.

VEDER, CH., 1957. Considerazioni sulla possibilità che fenomeni elettro-osmotici siano all' origine della formazione di particolari tipi di frane. Geotecnica, No. 5, Milano.

— 1963. Die Bedeutung natürlicher elektrischer Felder für Elektroosmose und Elektrokataphorese im Grundbau. Der Bauingenieur, 38: 378–388.

VOITESTI, I. P., 1934. Notiuni de geologia zăcämintelor de sare. Rev. Muz. Min., Cluj.

— 1938. L'influence de l'érosion sur la forme et la structure des massifs de sel. C. R. de l'Acad. Sci. de Roum., p. 412–415.

WAGNER, C. J., 1884. Die Beziehungen der Geologie zu den Ingenieurwissenschaften. Spielhagen & Schurich, Wien, 88 pp.

WALTERS, R. C. S., 1962. Dam geology. Butterworth, London, 334 pp.

WARD, W. H., 1945. The stability of natural slopes. Geograph. Journal, London. 105: 170–196.

WATZNAUER, A., 1965. Die Rutschung von Nieder-Tenzel (1941) — Eine Korrektur. Zeitschr. f. angew. Geol., 11: 667–668.

WOLDŘICH, J. N., 1899. Sesutí u Klapého z r. 1898. Věstník král. čes. spol. nauk, Praha.

YAKOVLEV, A. S., et al., 1954. Metodicheskoe rukovodstvo po izucheniyu i geologicheskoi semke chetvertichnykh otlozhenii. Moskva.

ZÁRUBA, Q., 1922. Studie o sesuvných terénech na Vsatsku a Valašsku. Čas. Mor. Musea zem., 20, Brno.

— 1923. Studie o sesouvání půdy na Hlučínsku. Tech. obzor, 32: 1–5, 17–20.

— 1926. Sesouvání půdy v oblasti českého útvaru křídového. Přerov nad Labem. Věstník St. geol. úst., 2: 226–235.

— 1927. Sesouvání železničního náspu u Podlešína. Zprávy veř. služby techn., 9: 602–607.

— 1929a. Quelques terrains de glissement dans la République Tchécoslovaque. Second Congress of Slav. geographs in Poland, Kraków, pp. 276–289.

— 1929b. Příspěvek k významu geologie pro městské stavby komunikační. Věstník st. geol. úst., 5: 294–304.

— 1931. O stabilitě svahů nad povltavskou silnicí u Štěchovic a Vraného. Techn. obzor. 39: 293–297, 330/333.

— 1932. Výzkumné práce geologické v inženýrském stavitelství (Geological investigations in civil engineering). Masaryk. Akad. práce, Praha, pp. 144.

— 1933. Sesouvání svahů pod Andělkou ve Střešovicích. Věstník hl. m. Prahy, pp. 229–259.

— 1934. Hráze na řece San Gabriel v Kalifornii. Tech. obzor, 42: 357–359, 394–396.

— 1936. Vliv klimatických poměrů na smršťování křídových slínů. Věda přírodní, 17: 217–221.

210

— 1938. Sesuvy v Lyském průsmyku a jejich význam pro komunikační stavby. Tech. obzor, 73: 1–6, 26–29.

— 1943. Periglaciální zjevy v okolí Prahy. Rozpravy Č. Akademie, Praha, 34 pp.

— 1952. Periglaciální zjevy na Turnovsku. Sborník ÚÚG, 19: 157–168.

— 1954. Sesuvy v neogenních uloženinách na severním okraji turčanské kotliny. Věstník ÚÚG, 24: 77–84.

— 1956. Deformace hornin vzniklé vytlačováním podloží. Rozpravy ČSAV, 66/15, 35 pp.

— 1958a. Bulged valleys and their importance for foundation of dams. VI. Intern. Congress on Large Dams. New York, pp. 509–515.

— 1958b. Pleistocenní naduřování vrstev v údolí řeky Arges v Rumunsku. Věstník ÚÚG, 13: 412–419.

— 1960. Plastische Verformung von Schichten in Tälern und ihre Bedeutung für die Gründung von Bauwerken. Zeitsch. f. angew. Geol., 60: 425–428.

— 1961. Glaukonit, ein Faktor der erhöhten Neigung zu Rutschungen. Bergakad. Freiberg. 13: 175–181.

— 1962. Zaostává metodika geologického průzkumu při zakládání? Vodní hospodářství, 8: 344–346.

ZÁRUBA, Q., ANDRUSOV, D., 1936. Zpráva o výzkumu sesuvného území na hlavní dráze Banská Bystrica—Diviaky. Manuscript.

ZÁRUBA, Q., FENCL, J., 1960. Geologický výzkum zátopné oblasti orlické zdrže. — Sborník vědeckých prací k 70. naroz. akad. T. Ježdíka, Praha, p. 221–239.

ZÁRUBA, Q., FENCL, J., EISENSTEIN, Z., ŠIMEK, J., 1966. Rozbor sesuvu u Dnebohu. Sborník HIG, 5: 141–160.

ZÁRUBA, Q., LOŽEK, V., 1966a. Skalním zřícením hrazené jezero v údolí Blatné u Lubochně. Věstník ÚÚG, 41: 375–377.

— 1966b. Interglaciální limnické uloženiny u Mikšové nad Váhem. Věstník ÚÚG, 41: 45–50.

ZÁRUBA, Q., MENCL, V., 1954. Inženýrská geologie. ČSAV, Praha, 486 pp.

— 1958. Rozbor sesuvu u Klačan na Váhu. Rozpravy ČSAV, 68: 31 pp.

— 1961. Ingenieurgeologie. Akademie Ver., Berlin, 606 pp.

ZÁRUBA, Q., NOVOSAD, S., TYROLEROVÁ, P., 1963. Deformace godulských pískovců na údolním svahu řeky Morávky v Beskydech. In: Metodika inž. geol. výzkumu pevných hornin. Academia, Praha, pp. 118–126.

ZÁRUBA, Q., TYROLEROVÁ, P., 1960. Význam glaukonitu pro sesouvání půdy. Věstník ÚÚG, 35: 475–478.

ZELLER, 1924. Bahnbau im Rutschgebiet. Die Bautechnik, 2: 599–614.

ZISCHINSKY, U., 1966a. On the deformation of high slopes. Internat. Congress on Rock Mech. Lisabon, 2: 175–185.

— 1966b. Bewegungsbilder instabiler Talflanken. Mitt. Ges. Geol. Bergbaustud., Wien, 17: 127–167.

ZOLOTAREV, G. S., 1964. Geneticheskie tipy opolznei, ikh razvitie i izuchenie. In: Materialy Sov. vop. izucheniya opolznei i mer borby s nimi. Kiev, pp. 165–170.

ZOUBEK, V., 1953. Geologické podklady k projektu údolní přehrady u Orlických Zlákovic. Geotechnica 15, Praha, 123 pp.

ŽEBERA, K., 1958. Soupis sesuvných území a sesuvů v oblasti na jih od Ostravy. Anthropozoikum, 7: 231–240.

INDEX

Frost action, 75
— effects, 27

Geological investigation, 95
— structure, 95
Glauconite, 71, 117
Glauconitic rocks, 102
Gravitational slides, 85, 86
Gravity collapse structures, 87
Ground water, 24, 27
Grouting, 161
Gullies, 187

Hammer test, 112
Hangtektonik, 78
Head scarp, 22, 59, 96
Highroad failure, 7
Horizontal borehole, 173
— displacement, 61
Horsetail 102
Hydrogeological observations, 52
— research, 104
Hydrotechnic structures, 167

Illite, 116, 117
Indicator plants, 103
Intra-Carpathian depressions, 185
Ion-exchange process, 117

Kaolinite, 117
Keuper clay, 193
Klippen Belt, 40, 188

Laboratory investigation, 111
Lakes dammed, 13, 82
— temporary, 3
Landslide Bánovce, 110, 150, 151
— Březno, 182
— Dneboh, 5
— Dubková, 5, 102
— Folkestone, 63, 64
— Flims, 11, 79
— Goldau, 80
— Gros Ventre, 13, 81
— Hazmburk, 4, 181
— Mikšová, 67
— Stadice, 180, 181
— Sučany, 60, 61
— Vaiont, 15, 81, 137
— Vaerdalen, 3
— Volga type, 63
Landslides active, 98, 100
— along predetermined surfaces, 66
— asequent, 31
— buried, 33
— consequent, 31, 106
— contemporary, 33
— dormant, 33
— exhausted, 33
— fossil, 33
— in pelitic rocks, 58
— in the Bohemian Massif, 175
— in the Carpathian area 185

Landslides in the Cretaecous formation of
  Bohemia, 177
— — — České středohoří Mts., 179
— — — Intra-Carpathian depressions, 192
— insequent, 31, 106
— on seashores, 15, 58, 63
— retrogressive, 23
— sheet, 25
— stabilized, 33
Lateral ridges, 96
Leda clay, 92
Liquefaction of sand, 57
Loading embankment, 139
Loess, 101, 171
Long-term deformation, 85, 87

Map of landslides, 174
Mapping of landslide, 95
Measurement of profiles, 47
— — the rate of movement, 46
Modulus of deformation, 120, 121
Mohr's circles, 20, 124, 119
Montmorillonite, 116
Montmorillonitic clays, 120
Mudflow, 100
— volcanic, 58
Muren, 53

Neogene clay, 4, 192
— sediments, 191

Ombrometric records, 30
— stations, 29
Open pit, 184
Opencast mine, 183
Ordovician shales, 57, 175
Outwashing of sand, 56
Overbridging, 153

Palaeontological methods, 103
Peak value strength, 119
Perenially frozen ground, 75, 180
Periglacial climatic conditions, 178
— freezing, 75
Permeability, 115
Permian claystone, 193
Pettersson's method, 132
Piezometer, 165
Piezometric tubes, 136
Piles, 157
Plastic deformation, 69
Pollen analysis, 104
Pore-water pressure, 26, 104
Postglacial landslide, 179
Potential landslide slopes, 102
Precipitation, 26, 28
Precompression, 21
Preliminary analysis, 123
Progressive failure, 20, 114, 127

Quick clays, 93
— sands, 58

213